→ Get your revision down to an exact Science

SCIENCE

GCSE PASS

GCSE PASS

Virgin

Robert Mitchell

VIRGIN REVISION GUIDE POWERED BY *Letts*

KU-722-924

Contents

Section 2 Chemistry

Section 3 Physics

Virgin Help Section

Welcome to *Virgin GCSE Science Revision Guide*. This unique pocket guide is designed to help your revision and boost your knowledge as you prepare for your GCSEs.

A team of revision experts has created this book to help you save time, avoid exam stress and make sure you get the **best possible result**. Here's how it works ...

Exam survival

Our expert advice on how to survive your exams will get you started; help you plan an effective revision programme; give you top tips on how to remember the key information; test your progress and reveal how best to survive the actual exams.

All you need to know

The information in this book is based on the core topics within the **Key Stage 4 National Curriculum** and all **GCSE exam specifications**. However, unlike textbooks or other revision guides, it covers the essential information in **just the right level of detail**.

The book is divided into three major sections: Biology, Chemistry and Physics. Each section contains specific topics you need to know to guarantee GCSE success.

Learn fast

Because each topic is presented on a single page, you can zoom in on the really **essential information** straight away. Start with the **Key Fact** at the top of the page, get to grips with the detail underneath and make sure you check out the **Grade Booster** comment before you test your knowledge on the opposite page.

Testing time

You've just read it, but do you know it? Well here's how to find out. Use the **Question Bank** to see if you really know your stuff. Check the answer section in the back of the book and if you got all the questions right, move on. If not, read the information again to see if you missed anything, then try again. Remember to revisit the Question Banks from time to time to make sure that the information has really sunk in.

Keeping your score

At the back of the book you will find a **Scoring Grid** where you can keep tabs on your progress. Keep your scores as you work through the book and see if you can spot any patterns emerging. For example, did you tend to get more correct answers in the human body part of biology than other topics? Then maybe you need to focus your learning more on the Ecology and Genetics sections. **Remember, these are your results – use them to get even better!**

And there's more

Want to find out more? Well help is at hand. We have included a **glossary** of key science words and easy-to-understand definitions plus a list of useful **websites** that will help improve your knowledge and understanding.

Don't know where to start? Can't remember the key information? Worried about sitting the exam? Read on and get your questions answered.

You already know more than you think

The fact is that you've probably already encountered the key information you need for success at GCSE. Over a two-year period, you'll have been taught all of the core topics on your GCSE specification and your teachers will have explained the course structure and how it's examined. You'll have done a fair few homeworks, tests and no doubt some form of coursework. All of this counts and shouldn't be underestimated. All you need to do in the run-up to your GCSE exams is to **revisit the information**, bring it to the **forefront of your mind** and **programme it into your memory**.

Make a plan

Use your class notes and put them into a logical order. You'll soon build up an idea of the topics you have to revise and whether you're missing any key areas. If you're still unsure about certain areas of the course, check this relevant sections in this book or ask your teachers – that's what they're there for!

Work out the time you have available before the exams and exactly what needs to be revised. **Be realistic** – don't kid yourself that you'll do 8 hours of revision every day for 3 months. You have to eat, sleep, exercise and have a life too! It may be a relief to know that **short bursts of revision**, say about 30 minutes at a time, followed by a break are the most effective. A **manageable plan** covering all topics and setting a realistic number of hours for revision each week is the way forward.

From time to time go back and **revisit topics** that you have already revised. This will help you check your progress and also it will lock the information in your **long-term memory**.

Finally, it may sound obvious but don't forget the importance of **noting the dates of all your exams**. This will affect what you revise and when, not to mention making sure that you turn up on the right days!

Top revision techniques

There are several proven revision techniques to help you remember information more easily. None of these memory-boosting techniques are difficult to grasp, but everyone is different and some may work better for you than others. Try them all and find the method that suits you best.

For most students this means making your revision as **ACTIVE** as possible. For example, simply reading pages and pages may not make the information sink in. Why not use the same system that we have used in this book: read a page of information, write some questions, have a short break and then test yourself.

In the same way, try some of these techniques to trigger your memory whilst revising:

■ Try condensing your notes into short, **revision cards**. You will learn as you go and you will build up a great library of Key Fact cards. For example, a card with all key physics formulae and one worked example would be very useful. Choose key words rather than writing full sentences. Break up the text with bullet points or numbers. Use a highlighter pen or underlining to emphasise the most important words.

■ Using **different colours** will help your brain store and recall information. Try writing in up to four different colours, but try to be consistent and, for example, always use blue for 'causes' and red for 'effects'. In chemical equations you could highlight different elements in different colours to see more clearly the different combinations of atoms.

■ **Be visual** – use drawings and labelled diagrams. A well-labelled diagram is an excellent way of recording information on a revision card. Diagrams should be kept very simple so they can be memorised and reproduced during the exam. For example, practise drawing series and parallel circuits to show the position of voltmeter and ammeters, plus an example of the volts and amps found at different parts of the circuits.

■ **Idea maps, flow charts** and **spider diagrams**. Simple flow charts and idea maps link information together, especially where there is a process or sequence of events. A few words in boxes joined by arrows are all that is required. For example, a simple process may be shown as 'meal $\Rightarrow$ food digested and absorbed $\Rightarrow$ blood glucose up $\Rightarrow$ pancreas secretes insulin $\Rightarrow$ liver removes glucose from blood $\Rightarrow$ blood glucose back to normal'.

- Drawing **humorous cartoons** makes revising more fun, and information easier to recall. To remember how current splits at a junction draw lots of funny round faces (each is an electron) which split into two groups where the circuit branches, and then rejoin.

- Make up **rhymes** and **mnemonics** to remember key facts. This is a very powerful way of learning and recalling information. A simple mnemonic technique uses the first letters of words to recall lists, for example, **R**ichard **O**f **Y**ork, **G**ave **B**attle, **I**n **V**ain for the visible spectrum **R**ed, **O**range .... **V**iolet

- **Repeat facts** out loud or why not try recording them onto a tape. You can then listen to them in different situations, e.g. waiting for a bus, doing the washing up, on the toilet! For example, the route blood follows: RA, RV Pulm art, lungs, Pulm vein, LA, LV, aorta, body, Vena cava, RA, RV ... Keep going round until you know them off by heart.

- Try **testing** a classmate, a parent or a friend. We all love a quiz and asking questions is a great way of boosting your memory. Agree with a friend to ask five questions each on the periodic table, and test each other the next time you meet.

  The more your revision involves you *doing* something rather than simply reading, and the more visual it is, the more information you will find you retain.

- *Test yourself*

  It may sound corny, but **practice really does make perfect**. As soon as you feel confident enough, you should attempt some practice questions. Try to familiarise yourself with the **style of exam questions** by highlighting the key words in the question. Get into the habit of **planning your response** before you actually start writing and then **checking that your answer stays relevant** as you write. And do ask your teacher for past papers and the mark schemes – in science *how* you use your knowledge is a skill examiners expect you to show, and seeing the mark schemes really helps.

  The thing *not* to do with practice questions is to attempt them before you have revised. Learn your stuff *first* and then test yourself. You will soon see the progress you have made or be able to identify any areas that you find particularly difficult.

The big day

If you've worked hard studying and revising in the run-up to your GCSEs, do yourself one last favour and make sure you **don't panic** in the exam.

Very few people enjoy sitting exams, however everyone can make the experience less stressful by remembering the following exam techniques.

- **Read the instructions on the exam paper.** This is obvious, but really, really important. Take particular notice of the time allowed for the exam and the number of questions you are asked to attempt, now divide the time available by the number of questions to get an idea of how long to spend on each. Make sure you do this for every subject and every paper.

- **Pace yourself** through the exam. Read each question carefully and underline the key words to help focus and plan your answers. Remember to check the marks available for each question and to allocate your time accordingly. And if there are two marks available try to state two things, not just one.

- **Stay calm** no matter what the paper throws at you. Whilst it is advisable to attempt every question, you can always leave a difficult question until the end and come back to it once you have finished the rest of the paper. And *always* make sure you read the introduction to a page of questions – it will include vital information.

- Finally, leave some time to **check through your answers**. Don't be tempted to cross out and change lots of answers in the last five minutes of the exam, rather use this time to check that your writing is legible, your spelling is accurate and that you've done the best you can.

Good luck!

We hope you find this book useful – and enjoy using it. GCSE exams are important and can be stressful, but if you prepare properly and do your best, you will succeed. Remember, once the exams are over ... well, we'll leave all that to you!

Digestion

> *The key ideas in this topic are digestion and absorption – make sure you understand them and how digestion leads to absorption.*
> ***Digestion*** *is the breaking down of food from lumps to small particles and then to very small molecules.*

- **Why do it?** Only very small molecules can be **absorbed** by the cells that line the intestine.

  Note: Fibre in the diet cannot be digested and is always lost in the faeces.

To absorb the food efficiently the lining of the small intestine has these features:

- Finger-like folds called **villi** (singular, villus) provide $10\,m^2$ of area. They are only $2\,mm$ tall and do **not** push food along!

- There are microscopic folds on the villi – called **microvilli** – which increase the area to $500\,m^2$. The more the area of intestine in contact with digested food, the faster it can be absorbed.

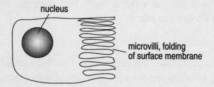

nucleus

microvilli, folding
of surface membrane

- Villi have a good network of blood capillaries to take the absorbed food away to the rest of the body.

- Only one cell on the surface of the villus separates the blood capillaries from the food – the distance for diffusion is therefore very small.

GRADE BOOSTER

Remember – diffusion is a slow process. To absorb food quickly enough the intestine has to provide a large surface area and a short distance for diffusion to take place.

Question Bank 1

1 Choose from these words to complete the sentence.

diffusion   faeces   absorb   digest   cells

Unless we **a** ....food we cannot **b** .... it into our blood. If food is not digested it is lost in the **c** ....

2 Which of these statements is true for fibre?

a It is absorbed, but not digested. ☐

b It is digested but not absorbed. ☐

c It is not digested and therefore cannot be absorbed. ☐

d It is not absorbed and therefore cannot be digested. ☐

3 Which of these features is true for the small intestine?

a It has a small surface area. ☐

b It provides a large distance for diffusion. ☐

c It is has microvilli that greatly increase the surface area. ☐

d It has villi that absorb large molecules. ☐

4 True or false?

Digestion leads to absorption.

5 True or false?

The capillaries in villi take away the absorbed food.

Enzymes

It's fair to say this is the most important topic in biology. Understand enzymes and what affects them and you'll gain an understanding of decomposition, respiration, photosynthesis and many other topics.

■ Enzymes are protein molecules that make chemical reactions happen millions of times faster (they are catalysts).

■ The key words you must use when writing about enzymes are **shape** and **fit**. Each enzyme has an active site with a precise shape, into which only one molecule fits.

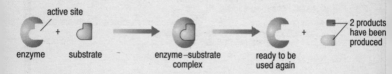

active site

enzyme   substrate   enzyme–substrate   ready to be   2 products
                           complex   used again   have been
                                                                  produced

■ The molecule an enzyme works on is called the **substrate**.

■ Each different enzyme is said to be **specific** because it can only work on one substrate.

■ Enzymes are not changed by the reaction they speed up – they carry on working.

■ At low temperatures, the enzyme and substrate do not collide as much, so reactions are slower. At high temperatures, enzymes lose their shape (they become *denatured*), and stop working. Somewhere in the middle (37°C for mammals) enzymes work at their best.

■ Most enzymes work best at a neutral pH (an optimum pH). Either side of pH7 they work less well, and will denature if the pH is too far from the optimum.

GRADE BOOSTER

Learn this: Enzymes are *protein catalysts* that speed up reactions. Each enzyme is *specific* to one *substrate*, because the *active site shape* will only allow *one substrate to fit*.

Question Bank 2

1 Why are enzymes said to be specific?

   a Because they are reused. ☐

   b They are denatured at high temperatures. ☐

   c Only one substrate can fit the active site. ☐

   d They are catalysts. ☐

2 Cover up the opposite page and try to add the missing words from this list.

   specific   active site   catalysts   substrate

   Enzymes are protein **a** .... that speed up reactions. Each enzyme
   is **b** .... to one substrate, because the **c** .... shape
   will only allow one **d** ....to fit.

3 Enzymes can work again and again, because:

   a They are specific. ☐

   b They have an active site. ☐

   c They are catalysts. ☐

   d They are not changed by the reaction. ☐

4 True or false?

   Enzymes are denatured by low temperatures.

5 Enzymes are .... molecules.
   Choose one term to fill the gap:

   a fat ☐

   b carbohydrate ☐

   c vitamin ☐

   d protein ☐

Digestive enzymes

*Make sure you learn the **word equations** for digestion. This is where many of the marks are to be had!*

To digest food, different enzymes are needed for protein, carbohydrate and fat. Because each food type is a different substrate, a different shaped enzyme is needed for each.

Below are the most important statements to remember:

- Starch is broken down by the enzyme amylase to maltose (a sugar).

- Protein is broken down by protease enzymes to amino acids.

- Fat is broken down by the enzyme lipase to fatty acids + glycerol.

*Important: you do not need to understand these reactions – you just have to **learn them**!*

But do try to understand these points:

- The reactions above are what happens when we digest food. The products (maltose, amino acids and fatty acids + glycerol) are small enough to be absorbed by the villi of the gut wall.

- Pepsin is a protease found in the stomach. It can only work in the acid conditions of the stomach.

- Fats are insoluble (think of a sugar lump in the mouth compared to a lump of fat). The liver produces special chemicals called **bile salts** that disperse (emulsify) fat into tiny droplets. This makes it easier for lipase to get at the fat because there is more surface area.

GRADE BOOSTER

Enzymes usually end with the letters *ase*, sugars end with *ose*.

Question Bank 3

1 Match letters with numbers from these two lists.

Food type	Is broken down to
a Protein	**i** Fatty acids + glycerol
b Fat	**ii** Maltose
c Starch	**iii** Amino acids

2 Pepsin is a protease that:

a works only in the stomach ☐

b does not work in acid conditions ☐

c breaks down fat ☐

d is helped by bile salts ☐

3 Fill in the missing words.

Bile salts help fat digestion by increasing the ....

4 Digestion produces molecules small enough to be:

a dispersed ☐

b absorbed ☐

c emulsified ☐

5 True or false?

Protein is broken down to fatty acids.

Functions of blood

*Everyone seems to know that blood circulates, but it's much more important to realise that **the job of the blood is to take things from one place to another.***
The blood picks up something from one part of the body and takes it to another part. A simple example is oxygen – taken from the air in the lungs to all the living cells of the body.

Here is a list of some other things the blood carries from place to place:

- Carbon dioxide from respiring cells to the lungs (where carbon dioxide is breathed out).

- Food absorbed by the small intestine to the liver (where food is stored or processed) and food to all other living cells.

- Hormones, including insulin from the pancreas to the liver (where insulin triggers the making of the storage molecule glycogen, from glucose).

- Urea from the liver to the kidneys (where urea is put into urine for excretion).

- Heat from where it is produced (e.g. shivering muscles) to colder parts (e.g. cold fingers).

Two parts of the blood are responsible for delivering everything:

1 The red blood cells carry oxygen and some carbon dioxide.

2 The plasma carries everything else including most of the carbon dioxide.

GRADE BOOSTER

When blood passes through most body organs (e.g. liver, kidney, lungs, intestine), substances are added or taken away. Think of the blood as a delivery system, and learn what's taken from place to place.

Question Bank 4

1 Match the letters with the numbers from these two lists.

a kidney   **b** liver   **c** lung   **d** pancreas

   i   excretes carbon dioxide ☐

   ii puts the hormone insulin into the blood ☐

   iii excretes urea ☐

   iv stores and processes some food molecules ☐

2 Which statement best describes the function of blood?

   a to carry substances in a circuit ☐

   b to transfer things from place to place ☐

3 Which gas is carried mainly in the blood plasma?

4 Fill in the missing word.

   The red blood cells' main role is to transport ....

5 Name a hormone carried from the pancreas.

Circulation and vessels

*Many students write things like 'the heart puts oxygen into the blood'. Blood has to be moving to carry things **from** one part of the body **to** another. The heart's job is to pump the blood around a circuit.*

There are two circuits:

- one from the heart to the lungs and back to the heart
- one from the heart to all the other organs (including the brain) and back to the heart.

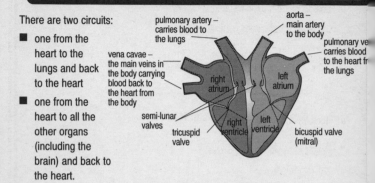

pulmonary artery – carries blood to the lungs

aorta – main artery to the body

pulmonary ve carries blood to the heart fr the lungs

vena cavae – the main veins in the body carrying blood back to the heart from the body

right atrium

left atrium

semi-lunar valves

tricuspid valve

right ventricle

left ventricle

bicuspid valve (mitral)

In both circuits the blood enters capillaries (blood vessels with walls one cell thick). It is here that things can enter and leave the blood (including: gases, food molecules, hormones, etc.).

- **The heart**. The main pumping chambers are the **left and right ventricles** (LV and RV). The LV has a thicker muscle wall to create a higher pressure to force blood around the body circuit. The RV forces blood around the smaller lung circuit.

wastes

nutrients

nucleus of cell

thin walls

carbon dioxide

oxygen

single flattened cells

Above the LV and RV are the **left and right atria** that pump blood into the LV and RV. Valves stop the blood going back into the atria.

GRADE BOOSTER

The blood vessels that carry blood away from the heart are called *arteries*; they have thick walls to stop them bursting. *Veins* bring blood back to the heart. Because the pressure is low, they need valves in their walls to prevent backflow.

Question Bank 5

1   What does the heart do?

   a   pressurises blood ☐

   b   pumps blood only to the lungs ☐

   c   puts oxygen into the blood ☐

   d   pumps blood just to the body ☐

2   Capillaries are suitable for exchange because they have:

   a   thick muscular walls ☐

   b   walls only one cell thick ☐

   c   valves in their walls ☐

   d   pressurised blood ☐

3   Which of these has the thickest muscle wall?

   a   left atrium ☐

   b   right atrium ☐

   c   left ventricle ☐

   d   right ventricle ☐

4   Which type of blood vessel carries blood away from the heart?

5   Which type of blood vessel brings blood back to the heart?

Gas exchange

*The ideas covered in this topic are quite simple; you just need to focus on a few key points. In our lungs, oxygen goes from the air to the blood. Carbon dioxide goes from the blood to the air. This is called **gas exchange** because one gas is swapped for the other.*

- Ideally we would exchange gases through our skin, but there is not enough surface area. The lungs provide an extra $100\,m^2$ of area in contact with the air.

- Lung surfaces are moist to absorb gases.

- The air has to be refreshed, otherwise it runs out of oxygen. So we breathe to ventilate the lungs.

- A huge number of capillaries line the air sacs to pick up oxygen, and lose carbon dioxide.

- These gases move by diffusion, which is a slow process. The blood capillaries are only separated from the air by one flattened (thin) cell.

Air goes out the same way it came in.

Learn this sequence: atmosphere $\Rightarrow$ trachea $\Rightarrow$ bronchi $\Rightarrow$ bronchioles $\Rightarrow$ alveoli (air sacs) and back again $\Rightarrow$ bronchioles $\Rightarrow$ bronchi $\Rightarrow$ trachea $\Rightarrow$ atmosphere.

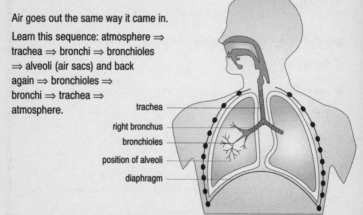

trachea
right bronchus
bronchioles
position of alveoli
diaphragm

GRADE BOOSTER

These key features of the lungs are also true of the intestines and the placenta: a *large surface area*, *moist*, *lots of capillaries* and a *short distance for diffusion*. There's no need to learn the same things more than once.

Question Bank 6

1 Which gas goes from the air into the blood?

2 Which gas goes from the blood into the air?

3 Which statement is true?

   a Lungs have a small surface area and are moist. ☐

   b Lungs have a large surface area and a large distance for diffusion. ☐

   c Lungs have a small surface area and are moist. ☐

   d Lungs have a large surface area and lots of capillaries. ☐

4 Which of these pathways is correct for air?

   a trachea ⇒ bronchi ⇒ bronchioles ⇒ alveoli ⇒ bronchioles ⇒
     bronchi ⇒ trachea ☐

   b bronchi ⇒ bronchioles ⇒ trachea ⇒ alveoli ⇒ bronchioles ⇒
     bronchi ⇒ trachea ☐

   c trachea ⇒ bronchioles ⇒ bronchi ⇒ trachea ⇒ alveoli ⇒
     bronchioles ⇒ bronchi ☐

   d bronchi ⇒ bronchioles ⇒ trachea ⇒ bronchioles ⇒ trachea ⇒
     alveoli ⇒ bronchi ☐

5 Gas exchange happens in the air sacs. What are these called?

Breathing and respiration

A lot of books use the term 'respiration' instead of 'breathing'. Make sure you know the difference. **Breathing** *is the sucking in and blowing out of air to obtain oxygen and to lose carbon dioxide – this happens in the lungs.* **Respiration** *happens inside living cells and is the release of energy from food.*

■ To breathe in, the lungs have to expand and suck in air. This happens because a dome-shaped muscle between the lungs and the stomach (the diaphragm) contracts and pulls the lungs down. For deeper breaths the rib cage also expands, pulling the lungs outwards. If we do both together, we take a deep breath.

But why do we take in oxygen and lose carbon dioxide? Study this equation for cell respiration. Learn it – it comes up often in exams. (And learn it backwards and you have photosynthesis!)

glucose + oxygen $\Rightarrow$ carbon dioxide + water + energy

This is what it shows:

■ food energy (glucose) is needed

■ glucose reacts with oxygen

■ the reaction produces two wastes – carbon dioxide and water

■ energy is released, **which is what the cells need**.

Why do we breathe more when we exercise?

If we exercise, muscles need more energy to contract, so more glucose has to combine with more oxygen. We breathe faster to get the extra oxygen.

GRADE BOOSTER

The energy released is used for muscle contraction and to produce heat to keep us warm.

Question Bank 7

1 True or false?

To breathe in the diaphragm goes up.

2 For a deep breath, which of these happens?

a Diaphragm goes up AND ribcage contracts. ☐

b Diaphragm goes up AND ribcage expands. ☐

c Diaphragm goes down AND ribcage contracts. ☐

d Diaphragm goes down AND ribcage expands. ☐

3 Which of these is the equation for respiration?

a glucose + oxygen $\Rightarrow$ carbon dioxide + water + energy ☐

b carbon dioxide + water $\Rightarrow$ energy + glucose + oxygen ☐

c glucose + carbon dioxide $\Rightarrow$ oxygen + water + energy ☐

d oxygen + carbon dioxide $\Rightarrow$ glucose + water + energy ☐

4 True or false?

Respiration is important because it releases energy.

5 True or false?

Respiration produces waste oxygen and water.

Homeostasis 1

*Our bodies are made up of trillions of cells that can only survive if the conditions are right. **Homeostasis** means keeping conditions constant, like body temperature, to keep the cells alive.*

Our blood supplies all living cells with what they need. So the levels of substances in the blood have to be regulated to achieve homeostasis.

What needs changing?	Organ responsible	How the change is made
Urea in the blood	Kidney	Excretes urea in the urine
Blood too dilute	Kidney	Excretes excess water in the urine
Blood too salty	Kidney	Excretes salt in the urine
Too much carbon dioxide	Lungs	Excrete carbon dioxide into the air
Not enough oxygen in the blood	Lungs	Absorb oxygen from the air
Too much glucose in the blood	Liver	Removes it and stores as insoluble glycogen
Too little glucose in the blood	Liver	Releases glucose from its glycogen stores
Body temperature too high	Skin	Extra warm blood goes to the skin surface to lose heat by sweating

■ How are these events controlled? It always involves this sequence:

receptors ⇒ control centre ⇒ effector

We monitor (check) on the levels of these things using **receptors**. Information from receptors is used by a **control centre** to judge whether conditions are normal. The control centre then activates **effectors** to correct the condition.

GRADE BOOSTER

Learn this example. We get hot when exercising. *Receptors* in the brain detect the rise in temperature and the brain acts as a *control centre* by sending nerve impulses to the sweat glands (*effectors*).

Question Bank 8

1   Name the organ that excretes urea.

2   Which of these is the correct sequence?

    a   stimulus $\Rightarrow$ effector $\Rightarrow$ control centre $\Rightarrow$ receptors ☐

    b   effector $\Rightarrow$ stimulus $\Rightarrow$ control centre $\Rightarrow$ effector ☐

    c   stimulus $\Rightarrow$ receptor $\Rightarrow$ control centre $\Rightarrow$ effector ☐

    d   control centre $\Rightarrow$ effector $\Rightarrow$ stimulus $\Rightarrow$ receptors ☐

3   Which of these is true of effectors?

    a   They continuously check on (monitor) stimuli. ☐

    b   They change conditions back to normal. ☐

    c   They directly connect to receptors. ☐

    d   They only adjust blood sugar levels. ☐

4   Which combination is correct?

    a   Lungs excrete oxygen, kidneys excrete urea. ☐

    b   Lungs absorb oxygen, kidneys absorb urea. ☐

    c   Lungs absorb oxygen, kidneys excrete urea. ☐

    d   Lungs excrete oxygen, kidneys absorb urea. ☐

5   True or false?

    We can cool down by sending less warm blood near the surface of the skin.

Homeostasis 2

It's a good idea to learn one specific example of homeostasis – this is a good one!

If the blood sugar level rises above the norm, the pancreas detects this. But how does it tell the liver to bring the level down? The answer is the hormone **insulin.**

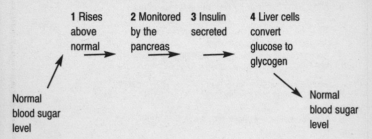

1 Rises above normal → **2** Monitored by the pancreas → **3** Insulin secreted → **4** Liver cells convert glucose to glycogen

Normal blood sugar level

Normal blood sugar level

1   This happens soon after a meal, as sugar in the diet is absorbed into the blood.

2   Blood rich in sugar enters the pancreas and the higher than normal sugar level is detected.

3   The pancreas makes insulin and puts it in the blood.

4   Blood reaching the liver contains insulin. Insulin stimulates liver cells to take up glucose and store it as glycogen.

■   Insulin is a **hormone** – but what are hormones? Hormones are chemical messenger molecules put into the blood by glands. A hormone allows one organ (e.g. pancreas) to communicate with another (e.g. liver).

■   The biggest mistake students make is to say that insulin converts glucose to glycogen. The insulin tells the liver to do this!

GRADE BOOSTER

Negative feedback is important to understand. We have normal levels (norms) for many internal conditions. If these levels deviate from the norm then mechanisms are activated to return the condition to the norm. This response is *negative feedback*.

Question Bank 9

1 Which of these sequences is correct?

   a normal blood sugar level $\Rightarrow$ insulin levels fall $\Rightarrow$ more glucose converted to glycogen ☐

   b low blood sugar level $\Rightarrow$ insulin level rises $\Rightarrow$ more glucose converted to glycogen ☐

   c high blood sugar level $\Rightarrow$ insulin level rises $\Rightarrow$ more glucose converted to glycogen ☐

   d high blood sugar level $\Rightarrow$ insulin level falls $\Rightarrow$ more glucose converted to glycogen ☐

2 True or false?

   Insulin is a hormone.

3 Which organ makes insulin?

   a liver ☐

   b kidney ☐

   c pancreas ☐

   d heart ☐

4 Hormones are:

   a nerve impulses ☐

   b chemical messenger molecules ☐

   c sugars in the blood stream ☐

   d always made of insulin ☐

5 True or false?

   Negative feedback corrects conditions back to normal.

Nervous system

For animals to survive they need information from the environment (**senses**). The information is used by a processing centre (**brain**) to take appropriate action.

The senses are:

vision   hearing   smelling   taste   touch   balance

(Six! Because balance has been added to the standard five.)

The key terms in this topic are: **receptors, nerve impulse, neurones, nerves, CNS and effectors**.

- **Receptors** are specialised cells that are sensitive to one type of stimulus – e.g. some taste bud cells are sensitive to sugar.
- If receptors are stimulated, they cause a **nerve impulse** (a bit like an electric current) in a nerve cell (or **neurone**).
- If you feel a complex shape with your fingers, then lots of impulses are produced, all travelling along separate neurones. The neurones are bundled together to form **nerves**.
- Nerves from receptors take impulses towards the spinal cord and from there to the brain. The spinal cord and brain are together called the **CNS** (**central nervous system**).
- Having received information from the receptors, the brain processes the information and sends impulses to **effectors** to take action. Effectors include muscles and glands.

Voluntary and reflex responses

If someone tickles your hand with a feather, you send impulses to muscles to consciously remove your hand – this is a **voluntary** response. If, however, you place your hand by accident on something sharp, the **reflex** action rapidly removes your hand, without you thinking about it. Reflexes also include blinking, changing the size of your pupil, erecting skin hairs, etc.

GRADE BOOSTER

Remember, the CNS sends nerve impulses to *effectors* to take action – effectors include sweat glands, muscles, etc.

Question Bank 10

1　Which sense is missing from this list?

Smell, taste, vision, hearing, balance and ....

2　Which of these statements is **not** true?

　　a　Nerves are bundles of nerve cells. ☐

　　b　Neurones are single nerve cells. ☐

　　c　Nerve cells are highly elongated cells. ☐

　　d　Nerve cells are bundles of nerves. ☐

3　True or false?

The brain is the central nervous system.

4　Which of the following is **not** a reflex response?

　　a　rapidly removing a hand from a red-hot object ☐

　　b　skin hairs erecting ☐

　　c　the pupil changing size ☐

　　d　a goalkeeper making a good save ☐

5　Which of the following is **not** true?

　　a　The spinal cord is part of the CNS. ☐

　　b　A nerve in a finger is part of the CNS. ☐

　　c　The CNS is the brain and spinal cord. ☐

　　d　The CNS includes the brain. ☐

Reflexes

The two examples of reflexes given here will help you understand the terms on the previous page – it's always easier to understand and learn terms within a real system.

Example 1

You touch something hot. Pain receptors in the fingertips send nerve impulses along neurones towards the spinal cord. To produce a speedier response, the impulses don't go to the brain – they pass straight back down the arm to muscles (effectors) to remove the hand.

Example 2

You are in the dark and someone suddenly puts on a bright light. The light has passed through the pupil and hit the light-sensitive cells at the back of the eye. These light receptors form a layer called the *retina*. Impulses from the retina pass along the optic nerve to the brain. Impulses return from the brain and stimulate the iris to constrict the pupil.

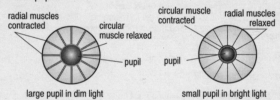

large pupil in dim light   small pupil in bright light

■ What is the purpose of reflexes? Quite simply, they allow for a quick response – to minimise damage caused by strong stimuli (heat, bright light).

They share the same basic pathway:

receptors $\Rightarrow$ nerve impulses $\Rightarrow$ CNS $\Rightarrow$ nerve impulses $\Rightarrow$ effector muscles

■ Why use nerve impulses instead of hormones? The answer is speed. Nerve impulses can travel at over 100 m/s, so responses can, literally, be split-second. Hormones tend to control responses that do not need to be as immediate e.g. control of blood sugar level.

GRADE BOOSTER

Imagine how difficult it would be to concentrate if you had to think about the size of your pupil – reflexes are unconscious responses.

Question Bank 11

1   If you touch something hot, the reflex response is fast because:

   a   Impulses go to the brain to cause a faster response. ☐

   b   Impulses go straight to muscles to move the hand. ☐

   c   Impulses take a shorter route, missing out the pathway to the brain. ☐

   d   Impulses are too slow, so hormones are used. ☐

2   If a bright light is shone into the eye:

   a   The pupil constricts because the retina has received more light. ☐

   b   The pupil gets larger because the retina has received more light. ☐

   c   The retina gets larger because the pupil has received more light. ☐

   d   The pupil constricts because the retina gets larger. ☐

3   Add these words to fill the blanks in the paragraph:
   nerve impulses, CNS, receptors, effectors.

   When you stand on a sharp object, this is detected by **a** .... in
   the foot, that send **b** .... towards the spinal cord, which
   is part of the **c** .... The muscles in the leg that move the foot
   are examples of **d** ....

4   True or false?

   Nerve impulses can travel at 100 metres per second.

5   True or false?

   Hormones provide quicker responses than nerve impulses.

Disease and drugs

*Disease is such a common word but is often not understood in its wider context. A doctor recognises an illness in us because we show signs (**symptoms**) of our body not working properly. If it's not working properly, we have a disease.*

Three things cause disease:

1 **pathogens** – other living things that cause illness (germs and parasites)

2 **genetics** – we may have inherited faulty genes, e.g. causing haemophilia

3 our **environment** – drugs, pollution and poor diet.

Note: These factors are often linked in a complex way – e.g. asthma can be triggered by pollution, genetics and other organisms (mites).

So, can we avoid disease? Not entirely, but the following do help:

phagocyte

- Natural barriers (e.g. the skin, stomach acid, blood clotting, etc.) all help stop entry of pathogens.

- White blood cells engulf and digest microbes, and produce antibodies to help destroy microbes.

- We cannot change our parents, so genetic diseases are difficult to avoid. But new techniques of genetic therapy are being developed.

engulfs and digests pathogen

- We can stop smoking – which can cause cancers, strokes and heart disease – and drinking (alcohol) in excess – which causes cancers and liver failure.

- We can avoid solvent abuse, which causes damage to lungs, liver and brain.

- We can also eat a sensible diet and reduce risks of cancers and heart disease.

GRADE BOOSTER

A lot of textbooks will contain more on drugs than this. Before studying them, check your exam specification.

Question Bank 12

1   True or false?

    Haemophilia is a genetic disease.

2   Our environment can cause disease. Which of these is **not** an environmental
    factor?

    a   drugs

    b   inherited genes

    c   tobacco smoke

    d   alcohol

3   Which one of these is **not** a barrier?

    a   antibodies

    b   stomach acid

    c   blood clotting

    d   the skin

4   Which of the following do we have no control over?

    a   diseases caused by our diet

    b   diseases caused by our genes

    c   diseases caused by alcohol

    d   diseases caused by smoking

5   Yes or no?

    Are harmful bacteria pathogens?

Diffusion and osmosis

These terms seem to come up in so many topics that they become familiar, but they're rarely understood. Let's compare them.

Diffusion and osmosis have some things in common:

■ they both rely upon particles moving randomly

■ by chance, particles are more likely to move to where there are less of them

■ particles tend to spread equally.

But they are two different terms – so what are the differences?

■ Osmosis refers only to the diffusion of water.

■ Osmosis is about water molecules (particles) crossing membranes through tiny holes.

Two examples of diffusion

1 A drop of ink in water. The ink particles, by random movement, spread out until they are evenly spaced.

2 There are more oxygen molecules in the air in our lungs than in the blood. By chance, more oxygen goes into the blood than out. (Do note that diffusion of particles is never in just one direction.)

Osmosis

The membrane is said to be **semi-permeable**, as it can only let the smaller water molecules through. The sugars on the right leave little space for water so the concentration of water is lower on the right. By chance, more water moves from left to right.

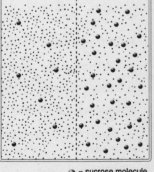

● = sucrose molecule

· = water molecule

GRADE BOOSTER

Remember – *osmosis* is just a special term for water diffusing – but don't forget to mention those holes in the membrane.

Question Bank 13

1   Which of these statements is true?

   a   Osmosis relies upon the random movement of particles;
       diffusion does not. ☐

   b   In osmosis the particles spread out randomly; in diffusion
       they do not. ☐

   c   In osmosis and diffusion, particles tend to move to where
       there are more of them. ☐

   d   In diffusion and osmosis, particles tend to spread equally. ☐

2   True or false?
    Osmosis is a term used for the diffusion of water.

3   When osmosis occurs through semi-permeable membranes, which of these
    is true?

   a   Larger particles move from a higher to lower concentration. ☐

   b   Smaller particles move from a higher to lower concentration. ☐

   c   Larger particles move from a lower to higher concentration. ☐

   d   Smaller particles move from a lower to higher concentration. ☐

4   True or false?
    Semi-permeable membranes have tiny holes.

5   When oxygen travels from the air in the lungs to the blood, this is an
    example of:

   a   diffusion ☐

   b   diffusion and osmosis ☐

   c   osmosis ☐

   d   non-random movement ☐

Leaves and photosynthesis

> You can get extra marks for questions that not everyone can answer, so don't ignore this topic! The key point about leaves is to relate structure to function.

Learn this table and you will have just about all the knowledge you require.

Feature of leaf	Function – in relation to photosynthesis
Waxy upper surface	Prevents water loss from the leaf
Transparent upper epidermis	To let light through to the photosynthesising cells
Palisade mesophyll layer(s):	This is where the light is brightest so most of the chloroplasts are here
Vertical rectangular cells, closely packed Numerous chloroplasts	Tall rectangular cells are better than a stack of smaller cells, as there are fewer cell walls for the light to pass through
Spongy mesophyll – loosely packed cells with air spaces between	Carbon dioxide can diffuse freely to the palisade cells above
Stomata in the lower epidermis	The guard cells swell and cause a pore to open in daylight – to let carbon dioxide in
Xylem	To bring in water for photosynthesis and transpiration, and minerals (e.g. magnesium to help make chlorophyll)

Photosynthesis

$$\text{carbon dioxide} + \text{water} \xrightarrow{\text{light}} \text{glucose} + \text{oxygen}$$

What limits the rate of photosynthesis? From the equation we have – a shortage of carbon dioxide, water or light.

upper epidermis

palisade mesophyll

spongy mesophyll

lower edidermis and stoma

What else can reduce photosynthesis?

1 a lack of chlorophyll to absorb light also slows the process
2 temperature – too cold and the enzymes work slowly; too hot and they denature.

GRADE BOOSTER

It's a common mistake to say that plants are making oxygen for our benefit – remember, oxygen is a *waste product* of photosynthesis.

Question Bank 14

1   True or false?

    Leaves have a waxy cuticle to stop water getting in.

2   Add these words to fill in the blanks in the paragraph:
    cell walls, **rectangular**, **palisade**, **chloroplasts**.

    The cells immediately below the upper epidermis are the **a** ....
    mesophyll cells. This is where the light is brightest, so most of the leaves'
    b .... are found here. These cells have a tall **c** ....
    shape, which means there are fewer **d** .... for the light
    to pass through.

3   True or false?

    The spongy mesophyll has air spaces to allow free diffusion of carbon dioxide.

4   What term is missing from this equation?

    carbon dioxide + water $\overset{light}{\Rightarrow}$ .... + oxygen

5   Which of these combinations will allow for rapid photosynthesis?

    a a low concentration of carbon dioxide, lots of chlorophyll and low
        light intensity ☐

    b a low concentration of carbon dioxide, lots of chlorophyll and high
        light intensity ☐

    c a high concentration of carbon dioxide, lots of chlorophyll and high
        light intensity ☐

    d a high concentration of carbon dioxide, lots of chlorophyll and low
        light intensity ☐

Transpiration and transport in plants

*These terms have special meanings in biology. **Transpiration** is simply the evaporation of water from a plant into the air. Not surprisingly, this happens mainly from leaves, as they offer such a large surface area, and pores (stomata) to let carbon dioxide in, so water gets out.*

Factors affecting rates of transpiration

- The air is dry (low humidity) – humid air cannot accept more water.
- The wind blows – in still air the air close to the plant becomes humid.
- Warmth – promotes evaporation, and warm air holds more water.
- Moist soil – if the plant cannot absorb water through its roots, it has to shut the stomata.
- Light – stomata open in the light.

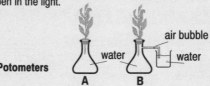

Potometers

With **A** the more a plant transpires, the more weight it loses. With **B**, more transpiration causes further movement of the bubble.

How and why does a plant replace the lost water?

- **How?** A huge surface area is provided by root hairs, which absorb water from the soil. Reinforced xylem vessels take the water to the parts transpiring.
- **Why?** If it doesn't, it will wilt as only cells packed with water (turgid) can provide support. Photosynthesis stops and the plant dies.

GRADE BOOSTER

What happens to all the sugar made? The sugars (and amino acids) are exported and travel via the phloem tissue to cells that cannot photosynthesise – e.g. roots.

Question Bank 15

1 True or false?

   Transpiration is the evaporation of water from the plant into the atmosphere.

2 Which of these combinations causes a high rate of transpiration?

   a air of low humidity, windy conditions, warmth ☐

   b air of high humidity, windy conditions, cool ☐

   c air of high humidity, still air conditions, warmth ☐

   d air of low humidity, still air conditions, cool ☐

3 Add these words to complete this paragraph:

   turgid, xylem, root hairs, water.

   Plants have a huge root surface area due to the presence of

   a .... which absorb b .... from the soil.

   Reinforced c .... vessels take the water to the parts transpiring.

   Soft parts of plants are supported by cells packed with water, the cells are said

   to be d ....

4 Which of these is used to measure the rate of transpiration?

   a a potometer ☐

   b a photometer ☐

   c a potatometer ☐

   d a photrometer ☐

5 Name the tissue that transports sugar from leaves to roots.

Reproduction

*One of the most commonly confused pairs of terms is **sexual** and **asexual** reproduction. Sexual reproduction is the term used used where a male and female have sex!*

- **Sexual** reproduction is when male and female **gametes** are produced and join (**fertilisation**). This does not necessarily involve a male and female – some animals and most plants produce both male and female gametes.

- In **asexual** reproduction the offspring are genetically identical to the parents (clones).

Each form of reproduction has an advantage.

- **Sexual.** The offspring are genetically varied and some could therefore survive in a changing environment.

- **Asexual.** The organism does not have to find a mate.

How is sexual reproduction controlled?

Most organisms have breeding seasons (e.g. lambs are only born in spring). As the cycle of events is relatively slow, hormones are used to control egg release and development of the uterus lining, etc.

The key structures are:

- The **pituitary gland** (found just beneath the brain), which releases hormones that stimulate the ovaries.

- The **ovaries**, which release eggs (ovulate) and secrete other hormones that cause the uterus lining to thicken. It is in the uterus lining that the embryo develops.

These events are natural, but humans can now use reproductive hormones to **control fertility**.

Some hormones stimulate egg release – sometimes too many!
Some hormones inhibit egg release – this is how the 'pill' works.

GRADE BOOSTER

It's easy to forget plants! Plant hormones are used to stimulate growth of roots and shoots to produce plants quickly from cuttings, and to control ripening of fruits (and the seeds inside).

Question Bank 16

1 Add these terms to complete the paragraph:
female, fertilisation, clones, gametes.

Sexual reproduction is when male and female **a** .... are produced
and join together, which is called **b** .... This does not necessarily
involve a separate male and female organism, as some animals and most
plants can produce both male and **c** .... gametes. With asexual
reproduction the offspring are genetically identical to the parents and are
therefore **d** ....

2 True or false?

Because reproductive cycles are relatively slow, it is appropriate for them to be
controlled by hormones.

3 Which of these is true of the ovaries?

  a They release eggs and secrete hormones to cause thinning of the
     uterus lining. ☐

  b They take up eggs and secrete hormones to cause thinning of the
     uterus lining. ☐

  c They release eggs and secrete hormones to cause thickening of the
     uterus lining. ☐

  d They take up eggs and secrete hormones to cause thickening of the
     uterus lining. ☐

4 Name the gland below the brain that releases hormones
to stimulate the ovaries. ....

5 True or false?

One way to control fertility is to use hormones to inhibit egg release.

Cell division, mutation and variation

Understanding the relationships between these three topics helps you understand each one.

A **nucleus** contains many **chromosomes** (in humans 23 pairs). Each chromosome has one long **DNA** molecule. Shorter sections of DNA are called **genes** (sometimes thousands for one chromosome).

- Most organisms have chromosomes in pairs.
- There are two copies of each gene – one on each chromosome of a pair.
- The two copies of the gene may be different – called **alleles**.
- Genes determine characteristics – different alleles control different forms of a characteristic (e.g. blue and brown eyes).
- One chromosome of each pair is from the mother, and one is from the father.
- Before cells divide, a copy is made of each chromosome – so each 'daughter' cell gets a full set.

Gene mutations are caused by ionising radiation (e.g. X-rays) and certain chemicals (e.g. tars in cigarettes). This changes an existing gene and is usually harmful – very rarely beneficial.

Differences between organisms – **variation** – is caused by just two factors:

1 genetic differences (mainly due to the combination passed on from the parents)
2 the environment (diet, accidents, disease, etc.).

Two simple examples – look at these graphs.

Student year groups will show this variation in IQ (intelligence). Lower IQ people may have genes for lower intelligence, but their environment (upbringing) will also have had an influence.

With blood groups, however, it is entirely genetic; no matter what we do to our bodies our blood group stays the same.

GRADE BOOSTER

Remember – because we have chromosomes in pairs we also have genes in pairs.

Question Bank 17

1   Which of these statements is true?

   a   Genes are found on chromosomes. ☐

   b   Chromosomes are found on genes. ☐

   c   Nuclei are found in genes. ☐

   d   Genes are found in alleles. ☐

2   True or false?

   Each chromosome has one long DNA molecule.

3   Which of these combinations is correct?

   a   Gene mutations are caused by radio waves and tars in cigarettes. ☐

   b   Gene mutations are caused by radio waves and nicotine in cigarettes. ☐

   c   Gene mutations are caused by X-rays and tars in cigarettes. ☐

   d   Gene mutations are caused by X-rays and nicotine in cigarettes. ☐

4   Variation is caused by two factors: our genes and the ....

5   Which of these pairs of characteristics is likely to be affected **only** by genes?

   a   eye colour and body weight ☐

   b   skin colour and blood groups ☐

   c   body weight and height ☐

   d   eye colour and blood groups ☐

Genetics 1

Most students find this topic quite easy providing they understand these two points: 1) in humans there are two copies of each gene; 2) each parent can only pass on one copy – so the offspring (children) also have two copies.

- The two copies of a gene you inherit may be different forms of a gene (called **alleles**).
- If one of the alleles is **dominant**, then it alone determines the character – the other allele (**recessive**) has no influence.
- Recessive alleles determine the character **only** if they are present in pairs.

Study this genetic cross:

Parents   Tall pea plants x Dwarf pea plants

F1 generation (offspring)   They are all tall

It should be obvious that the dominant allele is tall. We give this a capital **T**, and the recessive dwarf allele a little **t**.

Now remember, each plant has to have two copies of each gene. So we can add the genes like this:

Parents   Tall pea plants x Dwarf pea plants

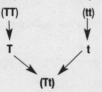

Gametes (sex cells)   **T**   **t**

F1 generation   **(Tt)**

Note: Each plant only passes on one gene – in each gamete.

(offspring)   They are **all** tall

The recessive character is hidden, but the allele is still there!

GRADE BOOSTER

It helps here to think about the plants' reproduction. Pollen from one plant fertilises another. The resulting seeds (hundreds) are planted, and the characteristics noted.

44

Question Bank 18

1 A rose plant has dominant allele (R) for red flowers and a recessive for white (r). Which of these crosses is most likely?

	Parents	Offspring	
a	RR x rr	All white	☐
b	Rr x RR	Half red, half white	☐
c	rr x rr	All white	☐
d	Rr x Rr	All red	☐

2 Which of these is correct?

a	RR = two recessive alleles	☐
b	RR = two dominant alleles	☐
c	Rr = two recessive alleles	☐
d	rr = two dominant alleles	☐

3 If T is the dominant allele (for tall) and t recessive (for small), which of these crosses can produce some small offspring?

a	TT x tt	☐
b	TT x Tt	☐
c	TT x TT	☐
d	Tt x Tt	☐

4 True or false?

We get one copy of each gene from each parent.

5 Which of these statements is true?

a	Each parent has one copy of each gene and passes one copy into each gamete.	☐
b	Each parent has two copies of each gene and passes two copies into each gamete.	☐
c	Each parent has two copies of each gene and passes one copy into each gamete.	☐
d	Each parent has one copy of each gene and passes two copies into each gamete.	☐

Genetics 2

Genetic disease is a sensitive topic, and we should be careful to remember that someone in the room may have a genetic disorder.

Mutant alleles are rare, but it is very likely that we all carry at least one mutant allele. Most mutant alleles are **recessive** – we can only have children with a genetic disease if our partner is also a carrier.

Name of genetic disease	What is the disease?	How it is inherited?
Cystic fibrosis	A disorder of cell membranes, often causing lung damage	Two parents without the disease can have children with cystic fibrosis if both parents have the recessive
Sickle-cell anaemia	A red blood cell disorder (common in areas where malaria occurs)	People with two recessives usually die young, but people with a recessive and a dominant allele can resist malaria
Huntington's disease	Affects the nervous system	Caused by a dominant mutant allele – the normal allele is recessive. So a dominant and a normal (recessive) allele = disease

Sex determination

■ Humans have 23 pairs of chromosomes – one pair determines the sex.
■ Males have one large sex chromosome (called X) one small one (Y).
■ Females have two large Xs.
■ Male sex chromosomes are XY, females XX.
■ Each sperm carries either an X or a Y – all eggs carry one X.
■ If a sperm with a Y meets an X we have a boy.
■ If a sperm with a X meets an X we have a girl.

GRADE BOOSTER
Remember: girl = XX, boy = XY.

Question Bank 19

1 Complete this sentence with these missing words:
   rare, carrier, mutant, disease.

   Alleles that have been damaged by X-rays or chemicals are said to be

   a .... alleles. Not many people have genetic diseases, as the

   damaged alleles are **b** ...., but it is very likely that we all carry

   at least one damaged allele. We can only have children with a genetic

   c .... if our partner is also a **d** ....

2 Which of these is a genetic disorder caused by a dominant mutant allele?

   a Cystic fibrosis ☐

   b Huntington's disease ☐

   c Sickle-cell anaemia ☐

   d Blue eye colour ☐

3 Which genetic disorder is associated with resistance to malaria?

   a Cystic fibrosis ☐

   b Huntington's disease ☐

   c Sickle-cell anaemia ☐

   d Haemophilia ☐

4 How many pairs of chromosomes do humans have?

   a 46 ☐

   b 92 ☐

   c 23 ☐

   d 2 ☐

5 Which of these statements is true?

   a Boys have an X and Y chromosome and girls XX. ☐

   b Girls have an X and Y chromosome and boys XX. ☐

   c Boys have XX and Y chromosomes and girls XX. ☐

   d Girls have an XX and Y chromosomes and boys XX. ☐

Genetic engineering

The technology of genetic engineering is complex, but the basic idea is simple. If a gene is transferred from organism A to organism B, then organism B will have a character typical of organism A.

How do genes work?

On a simple level it is enough to say they determine characteristics (e.g. eye colour). But inside cells their job is to determine which proteins are made.

Here is a real-life example of the use of genetically engineered bacteria. **Diabetes** is a disease that is often due to an inability to produce the hormone insulin (a protein). Study this diagram:

DNA from a normal human nucleus is cut up using special enzymes.

The same enzymes cut up the circular DNA found in bacterial chromosomes.

The two sets of DNA are mixed, and join together (assisted by different enzymes).

The mixed DNA enters live bacteria, which make human proteins – including insulin.

In summary, the bacteria have been reprogrammed by the human DNA and are fooled into making our proteins. By using large fermenters, large quantities of insulin are available for diabetics.

Engineering of animals and plants is possible but the genes have to be inserted early in the organism's life (e.g. an embryo a few hours old). As the organism grows from a few cells to many million, lots of the cells will have the inserted gene, and the desired characteristic.

GRADE BOOSTER

Use drawings in exams. Learn the sequence of diagrams above to answer questions on this topic.

Question Bank 20

1   Yes or no?

   Is using yeast to make beer an example of genetic engineering?

2   Use these terms to complete the sentences:

   mixed, DNA, protein, nucleus.

   DNA from a normal human **a** .... is cut up using special enzymes.

   The same enzymes cut up the circular **b** .... found in bacteria.

   The two sets of DNA are **c** ...., and combine.

   The combined DNA enters live bacteria, which make a human **d** ....
   e.g. insulin.

3   Which of these statements summarises the genetic engineering of organisms?

   a   DNA from one organism is inserted into another so that it
           makes a specific protein.

   b   Protein from one organism is inserted into another so that it
           makes DNA.

   c   DNA is removed from an organism and proteins are made in a
           test tube.

   d   Protein is removed from an organism and DNA is made in a
           test tube.

4   True or false?

   Genes code for proteins.

5   True or false?

   It is better to insert genes late in an organism's life to ensure lots of cells
   have the gene.

Natural selection

There's not much difference between natural selection and artificial selection. Both rely upon variation within the species and both require that not every organism has an equal chance of breeding. The difference is that people make the decisons about artificial selection whereas nature makes them in natural selection.

Let's look at a classic example of natural selection, the **peppered moth**. Study this sequence:

■ Trees are covered in grey lichen in areas of low pollution.

■ A peppered (grey) moth is well camouflaged on the lichen (otherwise birds eat the moth).

■ Industrial pollution kills the lichen and soot blackens the tree (birds spot the moth and eat it = selected against).

■ A chance mutation (you must never suggest mutation happens because it is desirable) results in a black (*melanic*) moth – which is less predated by birds.

■ Numbers of black moths rise (because they have been selected for).

The theory was all worked out by Charles Darwin (and Alfred Wallace), and their key points were:

1 All species produce more offspring than can survive.

2 Many die due to competition for a limited resource (light, food) or due to predators/parasites.

3 Organisms within a species vary.

4 The best adapted (e.g. thick fur against the cold) survive and reproduce.

5 The survivors pass on their genes, and the beneficial genes become more common.

GRADE BOOSTER

To be safe, learn an example of natural selection. Don't try to make up your own examples!

Question Bank 21

1 The main difference between artificial selection and natural selection is:

   a Artificial selection does not rely upon variation; natural selection does. ☐

   b Natural selection does not rely upon variation; artificial selection does. ☐

   c Artificial selection involves scientists deciding who breeds;
      natural selection does not. ☐

   d Natural selection involves scientists deciding who breeds; artificial
      selection does not. ☐

2 Which of these statements about the evolution of the peppered moth is
   not true?

   a Bird predation was the mechanism of natural selection. ☐

   b Soot blackened the tree trunks making the peppered moth visible. ☐

   c The melanic moth appeared due to a chance mutation. ☐

   d The melanic moth was a more dominant species and took over. ☐

3 True or false?

   The melanic moth is better camouflaged than the peppered.

4 Is this likely to be true or false?

   With a reduction in pollution, the peppered moth numbers have recovered.

5 Add missing words to complete the points made by Darwin and Wallace:

   vary, offspring, genes, adapted, competition.

   Species produce more **a** .... than can survive.

   Many die due to **b** .... for a limited resource.

   Organisms within a species **c** ....

   The best **d** .... survive and reproduce.

   The survivors pass on their **e** ...., and they become more common.

Evolution – the evidence

The problem we have in picturing this is that we only live for tens of years, but evolution usually happens over tens of thousands, or millions of years.

Evolution is the change of living things through time. As most evolution has happened millions of years ago, we have to look for the evidence in the form of fossils.

Fossils are the remains (or signs of the remains) of living things from many years ago. This usually involves burial in sediments until the build-up of pressure forms rock.

■ The hard parts (e.g. skeleton) are buried in sediment and are replaced by minerals that form rock.

■ Impressions of feet and roots can be left in sediment and then become encased in rock if decay is prevented by cold (e.g. frozen mammoths) or by lack of oxygen in bogs.

We only see fossils after long, slow erosion of rock or when layers of rock are lifted up by mountains forming, or when glaciers melt.

What do fossils tell us?

■ Species are discovered that do not exist now – e.g. dinosaurs. This suggests an extinction process.

■ Many species we see today are not found as fossils – they must have evolved from fossil ancestors.

■ Some modern species (e.g. horses) have fossil ancestors that show the evolutionary steps to modern horses (the oldest ancestors are found in the deepest layers of sedimentary rock).

Here are two recent examples of evolution:

1   The melanic moth from the peppered moth.

2   Antibiotics (e.g. penicillin) kill bacteria, but they are rapidly evolving resistance.

GRADE BOOSTER

Learn one good example of evolution – make sure the facts are in the right order. And don't suggest that organisms *choose* to evolve!

Question Bank 22

1   True or false?

Evolution is the change in living things over time.

2   Which of these is **not** an example of fossil evidence?

   a   the replacement of skeletons by minerals ☐

   b   the build-up of rocky sediments into layers ☐

   c   frozen mammoths ☐

   d   footprints encased in rock ☐

3   True or false?

Fossils can be exposed by the uplifting of mountains and by erosion.

4   Add the missing words to complete this paragraph:
   ancestors, evolutionary, extinction, fossils.

   The fact that some fossil species are not present today suggests that there is

   a process of **a** .... Many species we see today are not

   found as **b** .... – they must have evolved from fossil ancestors.

   Some modern species (e.g. horses) have fossil **c** .... that show the

   d .... steps to modern horses.

5   Which fossils are found in the deepest layers of sedimentary rock?

   a   the oldest ☐

   b   the softest ☐

   c   the hardest ☐

   d   the most recent ☐

Artificial selection and cloning

Today we have dogs ranging from Chihuahuas to Great Danes. Similarly, we have numerous breeds of cattle (Jerseys, Friesians, etc.) and many potato varieties. How has all this variation been achieved?

Study this bell-shaped graph for milk yield in cows – the largest yields are to the right. To improve yields in future generations you select the best milkers.

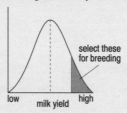

■ Breed the best-yielding cows with a bull whose mother was a good milk yielder. (These days, farmers select semen samples for their cows – the frozen semen may be from bulls that have since died.)

■ Measure the milk yield of the cows produced and breed the next generation from these – and so on.

There are problems, however:

1 Modern cow breeds produce so much milk that they would die if not milked by people.

2 By selecting for a limited number of characteristics that we desire, the breeds have **little genetic variability** – a lot of genes in the original wild cow, wheat, etc., may have been lost for ever. If conditions change (e.g. new germs evolve), we may not be able to produce new breeds.

Cloning animals and plants

Early animal embryos can be split into separate cells and each develops into a genetically identical animal (the wombs of surrogate mothers are used to produce lots of clones). Some cells in plants are not specialised, and given the right conditions will develop into identical plants.

GRADE BOOSTER

Cell division by *mitosis* produces cloned cells.

Question Bank 23

1 Which of these is **not** the result of artificial selection?

   a breeds of dog ☐

   b the melanic moth ☐

   c Jersey cows ☐

   d King Edward potatoes ☐

2 Add these missing words to complete the paragraph:
   mother, **yielding**, **generation**, **semen**.

   To improve milk yield the best **a** .... cows are crossed with a bull
   whose **b** .... was a good milk yielder. Farmers can select
   c .... samples for their cows. The milk yield of offspring is
   measured and the best cows are bred for the next **d** ....

3 Which of these is a problem caused by artificial selection?

   a Too many new genes are introduced into breeds.

   b Modern breeds do not produce enough milk to feed their calves.

   c Many genes are lost through selection.

   d This form of selection causes gene mutations.

4 True or false?

   The cells of early animal embryos can be used to produce many identical
   animals.

5 Cell division by mitosis can produce identical organisms called?

   a clones ☐

   b clomes ☐

   c cloves ☐

   d clines ☐

Adaptation

This word is often misused – students tend to think in terms of organisms adapting to conditions in their lifetime. This is not the sense you need. Adaptation is the result of changes in organisms over many generations (evolution). Natural selection pressures result in the evolution of adaptations.

Here's an example. Major changes in the world's weather have happened frequently in the past. The last ice age started 120 000 years ago and ended only 20 000 years ago. With these major changes in temperatures, organisms have had to adapt – or become extinct.

Animal adaptations to the cold include:

- thick insulating fur (or feathers) to trap warm air near the skin
- large fat deposits – for insulation and as a food store
- white fur as camouflage and to minimise radiation of heat
- hibernation and migration
- large size – reduces surface area to volume ratio.

Plant adaptations to hot dry habitats include:

- leaves reduced to spines to reduce surface area (reduce water loss)
- thick waxy cuticle to conserve water
- succulence – storage of water
- deep and extensive roots to obtain water over a large area.

GRADE BOOSTER

Here's a sequence of events to explain how organisms adapt:
Animal with thin fur ⇒ environment gets colder (for years) ⇒ only the animals with thicker fur survive and reproduce ⇒ genes for thicker fur are passed on ⇒ the average fur thickness increases.

Question Bank 24

1 Which of these describes how adaptations to the cold come about?

   a the evolution by natural selection of thick fur in polar bears ☐

   b the artificial selection for thick wool in sheep ☐

   c a short-term change in behaviour to avoid the cold ☐

   d the production by asexual reproduction of many identical offspring ☐

2 True or false?

   White fur can limit heat loss as it is a poor radiator of heat.

3 Which of these adult mammals has the smallest surface area-to-volume ratio?

   a mouse ☐

   b rat ☐

   c fox ☐

   d bear ☐

4 Which of these is **not** an adaptation in plants to survive where there is little water?

   a leaves reduced to spines ☐

   b a thick waxy cuticle ☐

   c deep extensive roots system ☐

   d reproducing in every season ☐

5 True or false?

   To evolve thicker fur, genes for thicker fur are **not** passed on from generation to generation.

Communities

*Most students find the ideas covered on this page quite easy, but do concentrate on learning clear definitions; a good example is the term **predator**.*

A **predator** kills other animals and then eats them.

Here are some other important terms:

- a **prey** is an animal killed by a predator
- a **scavenger** (e.g. vulture) is not a predator – it does not kill the animal it eats
- **parasites** gain food energy from a living host.

Predator–prey cycles

- As the rabbit numbers go up there is more food for foxes.
- Foxes multiply, and rabbit numbers fall – as so many are eaten.
- Foxes starve and their numbers drop.
- Rabbit numbers rise again as fewer foxes eat them.

Populations and communities

A **community** is all the living things in a habitat (e.g. pond). The number of animals of a species is a **population**. Different species have different sized populations, because of:

- competition for a limited amount of food or nutrients
- competition for light (plants)
- predation or grazing
- disease (parasites)
- the total amount of food made by the producers in that area.

GRADE BOOSTER

Don't think in terms of humans when answering ecology questions – the term 'community', for example, doesn't have the same meaning in biology as, say, in geography.

Question Bank 25

1 Which of these best describes a predator?

   a an animal that eats another animal ☐

   b an animal that hunts another animal ☐

   c an animal that kills and eats another animal ☐

   d an animal that eats another dead animal ☐

2 Add the missing words to complete the paragraph:

   eaten, up, rise, multiply.

   As the rabbit numbers go **a** .... there is more food for foxes, which

   therefore **b** .... Rabbit numbers then fall because more of them are

   being **c** .... Foxes starve and their numbers drop. Rabbit numbers

   d .... again as fewer foxes eat them.

3 Which of these best describes an ecological community?

   a all the people in a village ☐

   b all the species in a country ☐

   c all the organisms of all the species in a pond ☐

   d all the organisms of one species in a pond ☐

4 Which combination of factors is most likely to cause a fall in a population?

   a more competition and more parasites ☐

   b more food and more competition ☐

   c more parasites and fewer predators ☐

   d less food and less competition ☐

5 True or false?

   There are two types of competition: within species and between species.

Pyramids of biomass and number

*The ideas of **ecology** (studying organisms in their natural environment) seem easy but the answers required in exams are as precise as elsewhere. The key is to learn the specific meaning of terms, and to use the terms properly.*

All the food (chemical) energy in habitats is produced by photosynthesis.

This pyramid of biomass (weight) has 3 feeding levels and shows:

- the weight of all the grass grown in a field in a year
- the total weight gain by **all** the rabbits in the field in a year
- the total weight gain by **all** the foxes in a year.

The most common error is to assume it is the weight of one rabbit and one fox. There are many small rabbits with a total weight greater than fewer heavier foxes. The units for the graph would be $kg/m^2/yr$.

Here is a pyramid of numbers for an oak tree, caterpillars and small birds feeding on them. There are fleas on the birds.

This pyramid of number shows:

- a single oak tree (large) feeds many caterpillars
- the oak produces enough energy to feed many caterpillars
- each bird needs to eat many caterpillars – so there are fewer birds
- each bird supports many fleas.

GRADE BOOSTER

Think about the sizes and numbers of organisms in real habitats.

Question Bank 26

1 True or false?

All the food energy in a habitat is produced by plants.

2 The pyramid of biomass shows:

a the mass of all organisms in a habitat ☐

b the mass of single organisms in a feeding level ☐

c the mass of all organisms in a feeding level ☐

d the mass of single organisms found at every feeding level ☐

3 Yes or no?

Is it possible for a smaller mass of rabbits to produce a larger mass of foxes?

4 Yes or no?

In a pyramid of numbers, is it possible for one large organism to support many smaller ones?

5 Which of these is true for pyramids of numbers?

a The number of producers (plants) is always the largest number. ☐

b The number of consumers must always be smaller than the number of producers. ☐

c Top predators are always large so they tend to be in larger numbers. ☐

d A smaller number of larger organisms feed on a larger number of smaller organisms. ☐

Energy transfer in habitats

On the previous page you saw how pyramids of biomass and numbers look. This page explains why the biomass pyramid has to get smaller as it goes up.

As energy is passed from the producers (plants) through the various consumers, there are energy losses at each **trophic** (feeding) level.

■ The plants use up some sugars in respiration (remember – animals and plants respire 24 hours a day).

■ The food energy left is available to primary consumers (e.g. rabbits) in a food chain – but decomposers (e.g. fungi) get a larger share as plants die and trees drop their dead leaves.

■ The rabbits run around and produce heat to keep warm (both require energy from respiration – more losses). So not much of the grass eaten becomes rabbit biomass (weight). And most of the food is indigestible fibre, so more food energy is lost as pellets (faeces).

■ Finally, a fox (secondary consumer) eats a rabbit, but again the fox loses energy in the same way as the rabbit, so the total weight of foxes is small.

Note: The biggest energy loss in a habitat happens before plants make any sugars. Plants typically only use 1 per cent of the available light to make sugars, because of:

1 reflection

2 heating of the ground

3 transpiration.

GRADE BOOSTER

The more consumers in a chain, the less energy at the top of the chain. If you eat vegetables you will gain more food energy from a field than by eating animals grazing on the same field.

Question Bank 27

1 A plant is eaten by two herbivores and they are eaten by one carnivore. How many trophic levels are there?

a 2

b 3

c 4

d 5

2 As food energy is passed from one level to the next, there are energy losses caused by:

a photosynthesis and respiration

b decomposition and respiration

c photosynthesis and decomposition

d decomposition and transpiration

3 Why do mammals use up more of their energy than plants?

a Plants photosynthesise so they do not need energy.

b Only mammals carry out respiration.

c Mammals move around and produce heat for warmth.

d Plants can photosynthesise in the day and respire at night.

4 In the following chain, which of these is a primary consumer?

Grass ➤ Rabbit ➤ Fox ....

5 True or false?

Plants use 99 per cent of the Sun's energy to make sugars.

Carbon cycle

This can be a tricky one, but do remember that all you're doing here is pulling together ideas taught in other biology topics.

Carbon atoms are not destroyed on Earth. Every carbon atom in your body has been somewhere else before, and when you die it will go somewhere else. Here are the major stores of carbon on the planet:

■ in living things – carbon atoms can form long branched chains to form the skeleton of complex biological molecules – protein, fat and carbohydrate

■ in dead things (dead wood and peat)

■ fossil fuels – oil, gas and coal (remains of living things)

■ chalk (remains of the skeletons of marine microbes)

■ as carbon dioxide in the environment (produced by living things).

To move from one store to another always requires a process.
Here are some of them:

1 photosynthesis – living plants remove carbon dioxide from the air

2 grazing and predation – transfers carbon molecules from one organism to another

3 combustion – burning fossil fuels releases carbon dioxide

4 respiration (by plants and animals) releases carbon dioxide

5 acid rain on chalk releases carbon dioxide

6 decomposition releases carbon dioxide (due to decomposer respiration).

GRADE BOOSTER

Learn these two equations; they come up in many topics:

carbon dioxide + water $\Rightarrow$ glucose + oxygen   photosynthesis
glucose + oxygen $\Rightarrow$ carbon dioxide + water   respiration and
                                                  combustion

(You only have to learn one of them, and just turn it round!)

Question Bank 28

1   True or false?

   Your body contains carbon atoms that have been part of other people.

2   Which of these is **not** a reservoir (store) of carbon?

   a   coal

   b   peat

   c   chalk

   d   sand

3   Which of these is **not** a means of releasing carbon dioxide?

   a   respiration

   b   acid rain on chalk

   c   photosynthesis

   d   combustion

4   True or false?

   When a tree decays, most of its carbon is added to the air by the respiration of decomposers.

5   Name the compound missing from both these equations:

   .... + water → glucose + oxygen   (photosynthesis)

   glucose + oxygen ⇒ .... + water (respiration and combustion)

People and the environment

A lot of this topic is covered in geography, and some in chemistry – there's no point in learning the same things more than once.

There are more and more people, and people want a good standard of living. These two demands put pressure on the Earth in the following ways:

- destruction of natural habitats as we use the land for building, farming, quarries and waste dumps
- pollution caused by human overcrowding, burning of fossil fuels and industry.

Pollutant	Cause	Effect
Sulphur dioxide	Released when coal natural gas and oil are burned	Sulphur dioxide reacts with water in air and forms sulphuric acid. This falls as acid rain, which acidifies soils and lakes. Trees and fish die
Nitrates	Fertiliser run-off from farmland	Enriches river water, and algae multiply. When they die, aerobic bacteria remove oxygen from the water – fish die
Sewage	Cow manure and sewage farms – accidents on both	Sewage is food for aerobic bacteria, which remove oxygen form the water – fish die
Pesticides	Over-used to kill pest species	Washed into rivers where they can accumulate through food chains, killing top predators
Carbon dioxide	Combustion of fossil fuels and forests	As a greenhouse gas, carbon dioxide absorbs infra-red radiation, preventing it escaping to space. The Earth warms, climate changes and sea levels rise
Methane	Rice fields, cattle and waste dumps	Methane is another greenhouse gas

GRADE BOOSTER

Remember – when trees grow, they soak up carbon dioxide (a greenhouse gas) and store it as cellulose (wood). When forests are cut down, a lot of wood tends to be burned, releasing the carbon as carbon dioxide.

Question Bank 29

Match up pollutants and the causes with the effects.
Number 5 has been done for you.

Pollutant	Cause	Effect
1 Sulphur dioxide	Burning of coal and oil	**a** This is food for aerobic bacteria remove oxygen form the water – fish die
2 Nitrates	Fertiliser run-off	**b** Washed into rivers where they can accumulate through food chains killing top predators
3 Sewage	Animal waste on farms gets into rivers	**c** This gas reacts with water in clouds and forms sulphuric acid. This falls as acid rain
4 Pesticides	Over-used to kill pest species	**d** This gas absorbs infra-red radiation, preventing it escaping to space. The Earth warms, climate changes and sea levels rise
5 Carbon dioxide	Combustion of fossil fuels and forests	**e** This is another greenhouse gas.
6 Methane	Rice fields, cattle and waste dumps	**f** Enriches river water and algae multiply. When they die aerobic bacteria remove oxygen form the water – fish die

Cell structure

This topic usually occurs at the beginning of a course, but at the end you have a proper overview of how each cell type functions in a particular role.

Each cell part (organelle) has a different function. This is a 'division of labour', with each organelle performing one role. By keeping roles separate they are done better.

Organelle	Function or role	Where you have studied it
Nucleus	Made of DNA/chromosomes – to control the cell function. Or, better, to make proteins	Genetics, cell division, mutation, etc.
Cytoplasm	Where most of the cells reactions happen – controlled by enzymes	Enzymes in cells
Cell membrane	Controlling what enters and leaves a cell	Osmosis, diffusion
Cell wall	To strengthen the cell, and the whole plant	Support in plants, (plants only) osmosis, transport in plants
Chloroplasts (plants only)	Site of photosynthesis	Leaves and photosynthesis
Vacuole (plants only)	Store of water and minerals	Plant nutrition, osmosis

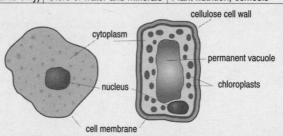

cellulose cell wall

cytoplasm

permanent vacuole

chloroplasts

nucleus

cell membrane

GRADE BOOSTER

Cells are made of *organelles* (e.g. nucleus), groups of the same cells are *tissues* (e.g. muscle) and *organs* are made of different tissues (e.g. liver).

Question Bank 30

Match up a cell structure with a function. Number 5 has been done for you.

	Cell structure		Function
1	Nucleus	a	A store of water and minerals
2	Cytoplasm	b	Turgid cells rely upon this to push against and support the whole plant
3	Cell membrane	c	Site of photosynthesis
4	Cell wall (plants only)	d	Where most of the cells reactions happen – controlled by enzymes
5	Chloroplasts (plants only)	e	Contains DNA to code for proteins
6	Vacuole (plants only)	f	Is semi-permeable and therefore controls what enters and leaves a cell

Cell specialisation

Having studied cells in each year of secondary school, it's time to pull your knowledge together. Cells are best understood by appreciating the different jobs they do.

■ Specialisation is vital – with each cell doing a specific job they do it better.
Here are some diagrams of specialised cells:

Cell type + label		Structure to function
red blood cell		large surface area. : vol = rapid diffusion of gases no nucleus = room for haemoglobin
nerve cell		extended = carry impulse a long distance
white blood cell (phagocyte)		phagocytic activity = engulfs germs
alveolus/capillary		flattened cells = short diffusion distance
cell with microvilli		large surface area = rapid absorption
root hair cell		large surface area = rapid absorption
palisade mesophyll cell		numerous chloroplasts = maximise photosynthesis
xylem vessel		hollow, reinforced = carry mineral solution

GRADE BOOSTER

Practise these drawings and learn the importance of the different structures. It gives you a different way of revising a lot of biology.

Question Bank 31

Match up the cell type with the structural features. Number 5 has been done for you.

	Cell type		Structural features
1	Red blood cell	a	Cells are flattened to minimise distance over which gases diffuse
2	White blood cell	b	The surface membrane is folded to form microvilli for rapid absorption
3	Alveolus cells of the lung	c	Biconcave shape providing a large surface area-to-volume ratio for gas diffusion
4	Cell found on the surface of villi in the small intestine	d	Dead, hollow cells with reinforced walls, which support as well as transport water and minerals
5	Root hair cell of a plant root	e	Carries out phagocytosis to engulf and digest bacteria
6	Xylem vessels	f	Single cells with an elongation to maximise surface area for absorption

Safety symbols

You're taught to be careful in the laboratory and to recognise the hazard symbols on equipment; but did you realise that they can be tested on your GCSE papers? Hazard symbols become very familiar, but you need to learn them by rote to ensure you pick up easy marks.

Here is a table with the symbols and their significance.

Hazard	symbol	The significance of the warning
1 Oxidising		By providing oxygen these substances help other things to burn more strongly e.g. sodium chlorate – weedkiller
2 Highly flammable		These easily ignite and burn e.g. ethanol
3 Toxic		These substances can cause death. They have their effects when swallowed, breathed in, or absorbed through the skin e.g. chlorine
4 Harmful		These are similar to toxic substances but are less toxic e.g. copper sulphate
5 Corrosive		These will react with living tissues/cells destroying them. Eyes are particularly susceptible e.g. sulphuric acid
6 Irritant		These substances can cause reddening or blistering of eyes and skin, but are not corrosive e.g. copper carbonate

GRADE BOOSTER

Use the learning of these as an exercise to practise your skills at rote learning. Remember – you only know it if you can accurately repeat it, or re-write it.

Question Bank 32

Pair up the symbols with the warnings. Number 1 has been done for you.

Hazard	symbol		The significance of the warning
1 Oxidising		a	These substances can cause death. They have their effects when swallowed, breathed in, or absorbed through the skin e.g. chlorine
2 Highly flammable		b	These substances can cause reddening or blistering of eyes and skin, but are not corrosive e.g. copper carbonate
3 Toxic		c	These easily ignite and burn e.g. ethanol
4 Harmful		d	These will react with living tissues/cells destroying them. Eyes are particularly susceptible e.g. sulphuric acid
5 Corrosive		e	These are similar to toxic substances but are less toxic e.g. copper sulphate
6 Irritant		f	By providing oxygen these substances help other things to burn more strongly e.g. sodium chlorate – weedkiller

Elements, compounds and mixtures

These terms will be used all the way through this chemistry section. You should learn the difference between them in order to understand chemistry topics.

Elements are the pure substances shown in the periodic table (e.g. C, Cl, Na). The smallest possible amount of an element is an **atom**.

Molecules are formed by atoms joining (bonding) together. The smallest molecules have just two atoms – e.g. oxygen gas (O_2), nitrogen gas (N_2).

Compounds are molecules made from atoms of different elements – e.g. carbon dioxide (CO_2) is made of atoms from the elements carbon and oxygen.

A **mixture** is just that – a mix of different molecules (or atoms). The air is the best example, being a mix of nitrogen, oxygen, carbon dioxide, etc.

Here are some boxes. Each box shows particles from one or two elements (one dark, one light).

These are single atoms of one element (e.g. argon).

Here are atoms from two different elements = a mixture.

Atoms of the same element have combined to form molecules (e.g. oxygen, O_2).

These are compounds, made of atoms from different elements joined together (e.g. carbon monoxide, CO).

Finally, this is a mixture of different atoms, molecules and compounds.

GRADE BOOSTER

Not all molecules are compounds. For example, CO is a compound, but O_2 is not.

Question Bank 33

1 The smallest possible amount of an element is:

   a a molecule ☐

   b an atom ☐

   c a compound ☐

   d a mixture ☐

2 True or false?

  Molecules are always compounds.

3 Which of these is a compound?

   a CO_2 ☐

   b H_2 ☐

   c N_2 ☐

   d O_2 ☐

4 Which of these describes a compound?

   a a mixture of atoms of different elements ☐

   b two atoms of the same element bonded together ☐

   c atoms from different elements bonded together ☐

   d molecules made of atoms from one element ☐

5 How many elements are in this substance? $Ca(OH)_2$

Atomic structure

The periodic table becomes familiar as you see it often, but to understand it you need to understand many fundamentals. The periodic table shows all the elements and gives their atomic mass and atomic number.

An **element** is a pure kind of substance, made up of one type of atom. Each element has its own symbol. Here are some easy ones to remember and two more difficult ones.

Symbol	Name of element
C	Carbon
O	Oxygen
K	Potassium
Fe	Iron

■ Every element symbol has one or two letters.

■ The first letter must be a capital – and the second not.

The structure of an atom

All atoms consist of up to three sub-particles – study this table.

Particle	Charge on particle	Mass
Neutron	Nil	1U (U = atomic mass unit)
Proton	Positive +1	1U (U = atomic mass unit)
Electron	Negative –1	So small it is ignored

■ Atoms have no charge, so the positive charge must equal the negative, e.g. if an atom has 6+ (6 protons) it also has 6– (6 electrons). They cancel out = no charge.

Atoms of hydrogen (H) are the smallest

1 proton in its nucleus

1 electron somewhere in this space

Atoms of the element helium (He) are the next smallest

2 protons and 2 neutrons in the nucleus

2 electrons somewhere in this space

GRADE BOOSTER

You just have to learn the symbols of some elements without any hint – K is potassium, Na is sodium, etc.

Question Bank 34

1   Which element is represented by the letter K?

2   For each letter, choose the appropriate charge –
    negative, positive or **neutral**.

    a   proton   ....

    b   electron   ....

    c   neutron   ....

3   If an atom has 6 protons and 6 neutrons, how many mass units (U) are
    present?

4   The mass of an electron is ignored because it is:

    a   so small (insignificant)   ☐

    b   a negatively charged particle   ☐

    c   not in the nucleus   ☐

    d   a positively charged particle   ☐

5   Which of these are found in the nucleus?

    a   protons only   ☐

    b   neutrons only   ☐

    c   neutrons and electrons   ☐

    d   protons and neutrons   ☐

Atomic mass and number

> *It's important to get atomic mass and number separated in your mind.*
> *The larger number is always the mass number, because it's the number of*
> *protons and neutrons added together.*

You will see hydrogen (H) and helium (He) shown like this:

^1_1H ^4_2He The top number is the mass number, the bottom the atomic number

The number at the bottom is the number of protons in the nucleus (only one in hydrogen).

The top number is the mass – hydrogen has one proton so its mass is 1U (see table). With He you have to add 2 protons + 2 neutrons to get 4U.

You can tell how many neutrons there are by taking away the smaller number from the larger. Here are some examples:

Element	Mass number	Atomic number	Number of neutrons
Boron B	9	5	4
Neon Ne	20	10	10
Aluminium Al	27	13	14
Phosphorus P	31	15	16
Argon Ar	40	18	22
Potassium K	39	19	20
Calcium Ca	40	20	20

Note: For many elements the numbers of protons and neutrons are equal (e.g. calcium) – but do not assume they are (e.g. aluminium).

GRADE BOOSTER

To remember how to calculate the neutron number, learn one example to remind yourself: for carbon $^{12}_6C$, 12 – 6 = 6 neutrons.

Question Bank 35

1   If an atom has 7 protons and 7 neutrons, what is its atomic mass?

2   If an element has a mass of 39 and an atomic number of 19, how many
    neutrons are there?

3   Sodium has 11 protons and 12 neutrons. Its atomic number is:

    a   1   ☐

    b   12   ☐

    c   11   ☐

    d   23   ☐

4   True or false?

    You can calculate the number of neutrons by taking away the atomic number
    from the atomic mass.

5   Hydrogen has an atomic mass of 1 (one). How many neutrons does it have?

Electron shells and reactivity

*You already know that electrons are found around the outside of the nucleus – but they are not randomly scattered. Electrons are found at different energy levels called **shells**.*

Remember, hydrogen, with an atomic number 1, has just one electron.

Note: The shell closest to the nucleus can only hold two electrons. The two other shells hold up to eight electrons (there are other shells, but this will do for now).

The first three elements

■ Hydrogen has one electron in its inner shell.

■ Helium has two electrons in its inner shell – which is now full.

■ Lithium has three electrons, two filling the inner shell, and one in the next shell.

Jumping ahead

■ Fluorine has nine electrons – seven are found in its outer shell – nearly full.

■ Neon has ten electrons – two full shells.

Reactivity

When atoms come in contact, it is their electrons that meet. Elements with full outer shells (e.g. helium and neon) are very stable – they do not like to react. **Atoms with shells not full react and gain or lose electrons to achieve a full outer shell.**

Here are two examples:

1 Lithium, with one electron in its outer shell, is more stable if it **loses** one electron.

2 Fluorine, with seven electrons in its outer shell, is more stable if it **gains** an electron.

GRADE BOOSTER

Take the atomic number and fill shells using these numbers in this order – 2, 8, 8.

Question Bank 36

1 True or false?

The first shell is full with 2 electrons; the second shell is full with 8 electrons.

2 Oxygen atoms have 8 electrons; how many are in the outer shell?

   a 2

   b 4

   c 6

   d 8

3 Which of these statements is true of neon (a noble gas)?

   a It has a nearly full outer shell and is therefore stable.

   b It has a nearly full outer shell and is not stable.

   c It has a full outer shell and is therefore stable.

   d It has a nearly full shell and is not stable.

4 Fluorine has an electronic configuration of 2, 7. How many electrons does it need to gain to fill its outer shell?

   a 2

   b 4

   c 1

   d 0

5 True or false?

The first three elements are, in this order: helium, hydrogen, lithium.

Isotopes and ions

> It's best to just learn these two terms. **Isotopes** are atoms of the same element with different mass numbers. **Ions** are formed when atoms either gain or lose electrons.

Isotopes

The periodic table usually shows atoms of elements with a specific mass number. In fact many elements can have atoms with different mass numbers. These are isotopes. Here are examples for carbon and oxygen:

$^{12}_{6}C$ and $^{14}_{6}C$ $^{16}_{8}O$ and $^{17}_{8}O$ and $^{18}_{8}O$

Study this table and work out what differs between isotopes.

Element	Atomic mass	Number of protons = atomic number	Number of neutrons	Totals
Carbon	12	6	6	12
Carbon	14	6	8	14
Oxygen	16	8	8	16
Oxygen	17	8	9	17
Oxygen	18	8	10	18

The difference in mass is due to a different number of neutrons – they add mass, but do not change the element.

Ions

Ions are charged particles. Remember, atoms have an equal number of protons (+ charge) and electrons (– charge).
Sodium atoms tend to lose an electron, leaving 11 protons and only 10 electrons. So sodium ions have a charge of 1+. They are shown like this: Na^+.

Notes

1   Some atoms form negative ions by gaining electrons (e.g. Cl^-).
2   Ions can be larger particles made of more than one atom (e.g. SO_4^{2-}, sulphate).

GRADE BOOSTER

Remember – *isotopes* **are atoms with different numbers of neutrons;** *ions* **are charged particles.**

Question Bank 37

1 The atomic number is equal to the:

   a number of protons ☐

   b number of neutrons ☐

   c number of neutrons and protons ☐

   d number of neutrons minus protons ☐

2 Isotopes of elements have a different number of ....

3 True or false?
  Ions are charged particles.

4 Add these terms to complete the sentence:
  electron, neutrons, negative.

  Fluorine atoms have 9 protons and 10 a .... The atomic mass is

  therefore 19. It tends to gain a single b ...., which gives its

  ions a c .... charge.

5 True or false?
  Compounds cannot form ions.

Bonding 1

Another vital topic – you need to understand how atoms join together. Atoms are held together by chemical bonds – which can be ionic, covalent or metallic.

Ionic bonds

- A metal atom loses one or more electrons to a non-metal atom.
- The metal atom becomes a positively charged ion (e.g. Na^+).
- The non-metal becomes negative (e.g. Cl^-).
- Then the positive and negative attract strongly = an ionic bond.

Covalent bonds

- Two atoms meet that are both short of outer shell electrons.
- To achieve stability (full shells) they share their outer electrons.
- Chlorine atoms have a 2, 8, 7 electron pattern (they need 8 to fill the outer shell).
- They share one each to fill each other's shells (forming the molecule Cl_2).
- This sharing bonds them together.

Metallic bonds

- Hardly a surprise – just metals do this!
- Metal atoms form positive ions (by losing electrons).
- The electrons lost from the atoms are like a liquid around the ions.
- The ions form closely packed regular patterns.
- The negative electrons bind the positive ions together.

Here are two diagrams to show the bonding of a metallic and ionic structure.

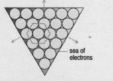

sea of electrons

• Na^+
• Cl^-

GRADE BOOSTER

Remember – atoms try to achieve stability by having a full outer shell, by losing/gaining or sharing electrons.

Question Bank 38

1 There are three types of bonding, ionic, covalent and ....

2 In ionic bonding, electrons:

   a are shared between atoms ☐

   b are transferred between atoms ☐

   c form a sea around the ions ☐

   d stay the way they are ☐

3 Magnesium (group 2) tends to form Mg^{2+} ions. How many electrons has it lost?

   a 2 ☐

   b 3 ☐

   c 4 ☐

   d 1 ☐

4 Chlorine has an electron configuration of 2, 8, 7. How many electrons does it need to fill its outer shell?

   a 2 ☐

   b 3 ☐

   c 4 ☐

   d 1 ☐

5 True or false?

   Metals tend to become positively charged ions.

Bonding 2

One of the most common questions about bonding and electron shells is to draw the shells of atoms and show how they form molecules with other atoms.

In reactions atoms often share electrons to achieve full outer shells. The sharing of electrons results in a **covalent** bond.

The main covalently bonded substances that you need to learn are: water, ammonia, hydrogen, hydrogen chloride, methane and oxygen. Below is a table of their electron configurations and what needs to happen to achieve stability.

Note: The full shells contain 2, 8, 8, electrons, which explains the 'sharing numbers'.

Element	Symbol	Electron configuration	How they share electrons
Hydrogen	H	1	Need to share a pair
Nitrogen	N	2, 5	Need to share three pairs
Carbon	C	2, 4	Need to share four pairs
Chlorine	Cl	2, 8, 7	Need to share one pair
Oxygen	O	2, 6	Need to share two pairs

Examples of ways of representing water, ammonia and methane.

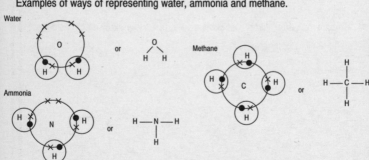

GRADE BOOSTER

In covalent bonding electrons are shared; in ionic bonding electron(s) are completely exchanged; in metallic bonding they form a mobile 'sea' between the atoms.

Question Bank 39

Choose from these terms to complete the three sentences:
ionic, covalent, metallic.

1 If the atoms are surrounded by a sea of electrons, this is .... bonding.

2 If electrons are shared between atoms, this is .... bonding.

3 If electrons are exchanged between atoms, this is .... bonding.

4 Which one of these electron configurations would be for an element that shared one electron pair?

   a 2, 5 ☐

   b 2, 7 ☐

   c 2, 6 ☐

   d 2, 4 ☐

5 Carbon has an electron configuration of 2, 4. How many electrons does it need to fill its outer shell?

   a 2 ☐

   b 3 ☐

   c 4 ☐

   d 5 ☐

Cracking, hydrocarbon combustion and plastics

The crude oil obtained from different wells varies, so it gives different proportions of each fraction. Some of the fractions obtained are more valuable than others – e.g. petrol is easy to sell, but bitumen is less valuable.

If an oil well produces a lot of cheap fractions, can anything be done about it? The solution is **cracking**.

The fractions containing larger (less valuable) fractions are passed as a hot gas over a catalyst. This shows some of what is produced:

Large hydrocarbons $\Rightarrow$ ethene (C_2H_4 – very small, just two carbons), propene (four carbons) and fuel molecules.

This breakdown is called **thermal decomposition**.

The ethene and propene can be used to make **polymers** (long-chain molecules) that are plastics.

- Poly(ethene), or polythene, is used for plastic bags and bottles.
- Poly(propene) is used for ropes and crates.

The fates of fuels

Combustion of	Combustion produces	Harmful effects
Methane, CH_4	Carbon dioxide and water	Carbon dioxide is a greenhouse gas
Sulphur-containing fuels	Sulphur dioxide	Acid rain

The fates of plastics

Being man-made substances, plastics do not degrade naturally (they are non-biodegradable), and they therefore accumulate.

Note: The reason why they do not biodegrade is because living organisms lack enzymes to break down plastics – they have never met plastics before, so why should they have a means of digesting them?

GRADE BOOSTER

Catalysts speed up reactions. The best catalysts are *enzymes* (from living organisms), but they cannot work at the high temperatures needed for cracking.

Question Bank 40

1 Crude oil is broken down by thermal decomposition. This is also known as:

   a flaking ☐

   b combustion ☐

   c cracking ☐

   d quaking ☐

2 Which greenhouse gas is produced by the combustion of methane?

3 Ethene can be made into which plastic?

   a propylene ☐

   b polystyrene ☐

   c polythene ☐

   d polycell ☐

4 Complete this sentence using these terms:
accumulate, non-biodegradable, enzymes.

Plastics do not degrade naturally; they are said to be **a** ....
Plastic rubbish will therefore **b** .... The reason why they do
not break down easily is that living organisms lack **c** .... to break
them down.

5 Which gas produced by burning coal causes acid rain?

Crude oil

This is simply oil extracted from the Earth's crust. It is 'crude' because it consists of a large number of compounds – the mixture contains mainly hydrocarbons.

Crude oil is a mixture of compounds – the chemical properties of substances in a mixture are unchanged, so the different substances can be separated.

Oil is made of **hydrocarbons** – molecules made of hydrogen and carbon only. The hydrocarbons of oil are of different sizes.

Here are two hydrocarbons – it is helpful to note that each carbon atom always forms four bonds.

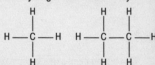

This table shows the five shortest hydrocarbons and their state at room temperature.

Name	Formula	State at room temperature
Methane	CH_4	Gas
Ethane	C_2H_6	Gas
Propane	C_3H_8	Gas
Butane	C_4H_{10}	Gas
Pentane	C_5H_{12}	Liquid

- The bigger it is, the higher is its boiling point.
- The smallest are the most volatile, the biggest the least.
- The larger ones are more viscous (flow less well).
- The larger they are, the less easily they ignite (set on fire).

To help picture these differences, think of petrol compared to tar (they are both mixtures of hydrocarbons).

- **Petrol** is a liquid (at room temperature), it evaporates readily (= volatile) and is easily lit.
- **Tar** is a solid, does not flow and is not easily lit.

GRADE BOOSTER

Hydrocarbons are molecules made of hydrogen and carbon only – remember 'hydro(gen)carbon'.

Question Bank 41

1 Which of these element combinations are found in hydrocarbons?

   a oxygen and hydrogen ☐

   b hydrogen and calcium ☐

   c carbon and oxygen ☐

   d carbon and hydrogen ☐

2 True or false?

   The boiling point of hydrocarbons increases with increasing size of molecule.

3 Carbon atoms always form a certain number of bonds. How many?

4 Which of these statements is true?

   a The larger hydrocarbons are more volatile, more viscous and
      ignite more easily. ☐

   b The larger hydrocarbons are less volatile, less viscous and
      ignite more easily. ☐

   c The larger hydrocarbons are more volatile, more viscous and
      ignite more easily. ☐

   d The larger hydrocarbons are less volatile, more viscous and
      ignite less easily. ☐

5 Which hydrocarbon is missing from this sequence?

   CH_4 C_2H_6 C_4H_{10} C_5H_{12}

The rock record 1

As we only see our world for decades, it's difficult to imagine the billions of years that it has taken to shape the Earth. You just have to accept that mountains have formed and eroded over enormous time scales.

The movement of the Earth's continental plates (**tectonic activity**) creates pressures that build up and distort the crust. Erosion by water wears away the surface.

Here is a simple key for identifying rock types:

1 Does the rock contain grains or crystals?

   Yes to grains = sedimentary rock

   Yes to crystals = igneous or metamorphic rock

2 Is the rock banded?

   Yes = metamorphic rock

   No = igneous

Sedimentary rock

These are the key points:

- Fragments of weathered rock are carried by water (streams and rivers).
- The fragments settle out in lakes/oceans, forming a sediment.
- The layers create pressure that squeezes out water, and crystals form, cementing the mass.
- The hard parts of organisms may become fossils – if rocks have the same fossils they are about the same age.
- Ripple marks in layers show the effect of currents or waves during deposition.
- The lowest layer should be the oldest, but tectonic activity can tilt and even turn over the layers.

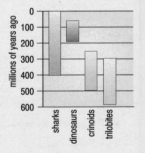

GRADE BOOSTER

Marble is a metamorphic rock and limestone a sedimentary rock – they both fizz in acid, because they both contain calcium carbonate.

Question Bank 42

1 What cements sediments together to form sedimentary rocks?

   a extreme heat and pressure ☐

   b tectonics ☐

   c pressure and the squeezing out of water ☐

   d currents ☐

2 True or false?

   The fossils found in a layer of rock are the same age as the rock.

3 From the graph on the opposite page, which group of fossils were formed between 250 and 500 million years ago?

4 Why can we not always assume that the lowest sedimentary layer is the oldest?

   a Fossils move about. ☐

   b Huge pressures and temperatures melt it. ☐

   c Tilting and over-turning can change things. ☐

   d Ripple marks can be confusing. ☐

5 Marble and limestone both fizz in acid. Which compound do they both contain?

The rock record 2

*When a tadpole changes to a frog, it does so by **metamorphosis** (changing its form). Remember this when you think of metamorphic rocks – they have changed from igneous or sedimentary to **metamorphic**.*

The huge pressures and high temperatures created by the squeezing of tectonic plates soften rocks and cause changes in shape and chemistry – but they do not melt.

Metamorphic rock

These are the key points:

- It is high pressure and temperature that cause changes.
- The changes result in rocks with a different **texture** and **structure.**
- There is no melting – otherwise they would be igneous rocks.
- **Recrystallisation** will have occurred.
- The rocks are banded – each band consists of **interlocking crystals.**
- Fossils, if present, will be distorted.
- Metamorphic rock in ancient mountains points to the huge forces that created the mountains.

Igneous rocks

Molten magma (melted rock) cools quickly in the air, forming rocks with small crystals (**basalts**); or cools slowly underground, forming rocks with large crystals (**granite**).

- Magma from below the crust $\Rightarrow$ cools quickly in air = basalt
- Magma $\Rightarrow$ cools slowly inside the crust = granite
- Sedimentary limestone exposed to high temperatures and pressures $\Rightarrow$ marble (used for floors)
- Sedimentary mudstone exposed to high temperatures and pressures $\Rightarrow$ slate (used on roofs)

GRADE BOOSTER

Igneous rock that cools quickly at the surface (in air) is called *extrusive* igneous. If it cools slowly beneath the surface it is *intrusive* igneous.

Question Bank 43

1   Add these missing words in the places provided:

temperature, **recrystallisation**, **texture**, **melting**.

With metamorphic rocks it is the high pressure and **a** .... that

cause changes. The changes result in rocks with a different

b .... and **structure.**

There is no **c** .... – otherwise they would be igneous rocks. New

crystals form; this is called **d** ....

2   What is the missing word?

Bands are formed from interlocking ....

3   If fossils are present in metamorphic rock, they will have been:

   a   shifted

   b   tilted

   c   melted

   d   distorted

4   True or false?

Granite has larger crystals than basalt.

5   Where do extrusive igneous rocks cool?

Rocks and their products

If you go to different parts of the country you will find buildings made of different (local) materials. Why? Because rocks and bricks are heavy and therefore expensive to transport over long distances.

Limestone (calcium carbonate) is the source of many of the most important building materials, including cement, concrete, mortar and glass. Shown below are the steps required to make these materials.

Mortar

Limestone $\Rightarrow$ heated strongly $\Rightarrow$ thermal decomposition $\Rightarrow$ quicklime (CaO) + CO_2

Quicklime + water $\Rightarrow$ slaked lime, $Ca(OH)_2$, add sand $\Rightarrow$ mortar

$CaCO_3 \Rightarrow CaO + CO_2$

$CaO + H_2O \Rightarrow Ca(OH)_2$

Note: Water is added to make a paste of mortar, as it dries it absorbs CO_2 and forms long calcium carbonate crystals. The mortar has now set.

Cement

Limestone and clay $\Rightarrow$ heated strongly $\Rightarrow$ a mix of calcium and aluminium silicates $\Rightarrow$ add water $\Rightarrow$ slaked lime produced, that sets like mortar

Concrete

Cement mixed with sand and small stones

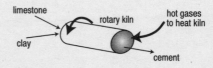

Glass

Limestone + sand + sodium carbonate $\Rightarrow$ melted $\Rightarrow$ cools $\Rightarrow$ glass

Other uses of limestone and its products

- Powdered limestone can be used to neutralise acidic lakes.
- Slaked lime (calcium hydroxide) is used to neutralise acid soils.

GRADE BOOSTER

Thermal decomposition (breaking down by heating) is one of the main types of chemical reaction that you must learn. There is an example on this page; but also see 'Cracking', on page 88.

Question Bank 44

1 Quicklime has which formula?

a $C(OH)_2$ ☐

b $Ca(OH)_2$ ☐

c CaO ☐

d $CaCO_2$ ☐

2 When limestone is heated strongly it is broken down. What is this reaction called?

3 Fill in the blanks below.

To make concrete, sand and .... are added to cement.

4 In the following, which component is missing from the mixture needed to make glass?

.... , sand and sodium carbonate

5 Which of these is used to neutralise acid soils?

a quicklime ☐

b acid rain ☐

c slaked lime ☐

d lime juice ☐

Extracting metals from ores

If you lost a gold ring, you could find it years later and it would look the same. A ring made of copper or iron would tarnish or rust. What does this tell us about different metals?

All metals can be put in a **reactivity series** from least to most reactive. Gold is not reactive; iron reacts much more readily. So metals like iron are always found combined with other elements.

Mining gold and other metals

Gold can be found lying around as pure gold – e.g. in some streams. Most metals, though, are found combined with other elements as **ores**. Strictly, an ore is a concentrated source of a metal that is economic to mine.

How iron is obtained from iron ore

These are the key events/steps:

- iron ore (haematite), coke and limestone are added to the blast furnace

- hot air is blown in to encourage the coke to burn

- coke combusts and releases heat and carbon dioxide

- coke and carbon dioxide react to form carbon monoxide

- carbon monoxide reduces the iron oxide to pure liquid iron

- the carbon monoxide and oxygen (from the iron) form carbon dioxide (i.e. oxidation)

- the limestone removes acidic impurities, forming slag that floats on the molten iron.

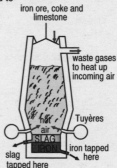

iron ore, coke and limestone

waste gases to heat up incoming air

hot air

Tuyères

SLAG

IRON

slag tapped here

iron tapped here

GRADE BOOSTER

Carbon is a more reactive element than iron, so it can remove the oxygen (*reduction*) from the iron.

Question Bank 45

1 True or false?

   Gold is less reactive than iron.

2 Which of these is the correct definition of an ore?

   a An ore is a concentrated source of a metal that is economic to mine.

   b An ore is a source of a metal that is uneconomic to mine.

   c An ore is an unconcentrated source of a metal that is economic
      to mine.

   d An ore is a concentrated source of a metal that is uneconomic
      to mine.

3 Which of these is the proper name for iron ore?

   a haemoglobin

   b haemolysis

   c haematite

   d haemabright

4 True or false?

   Carbon monoxide reacts with oxygen to form carbon dioxide. This is an
   example of oxidation.

5 When slag forms, what is removed to leave molten iron?

   a acidic impurities

   b alkaline impurities

   c carbon monoxide

   d heat and coke

Metals from ores – electrolysis

The simplest way to understand the basic principles here is to remember that the more reactive the metal, the harder it holds onto other elements. Metals like aluminium are much more reactive than iron and can only be separated from their ore by electrolysis.

Here are the key points to understand:

- Aluminium oxide is purified from aluminium ore (**bauxite**).

- Aluminium oxide is dissolved in a substance called cryolite. This allows the aluminium ions to move around.

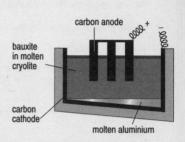

- A negative carbon electrode (**cathode**) attracts positive aluminium ions (Al^{3+}). At this electrode, molten aluminium metal forms by reduction.

- At the positive carbon electrode (the **anode**), oxygen forms, which reacts with the carbon to form carbon dioxide (this electrode has to be replaced often).

$$Al^{3+} + 3e^- \Rightarrow Al$$

$$2O^{2-} \Rightarrow O_2 + 4e^-$$

Metal corrosion and its prevention

It may have occurred to you that if aluminium is more reactive than iron, why doesn't it rust (corrode)? If you look at an aluminium saucepan, you will notice it is grey – this is a thin coat of oxide that forms a barrier, preventing further corrosion.

Iron will rust away unless protected by a surface metal that is less reactive, e.g. zinc, to form **galvanised iron**.

GRADE BOOSTER

This will help you to remember: the cathode (CA) is negative (NE) = CANE. Metal ions are positive, so the metal forms at the cathode.

Question Bank 46

1   What is aluminium ore called?

2   During electrolysis, what forms at each electrode?

   a   aluminium at the anode; oxygen at the cathode   ☐

   b   carbon at the anode; aluminium at the cathode   ☐

   c   oxygen at the anode; aluminium at the cathode   ☐

   d   oxygen at the anode; carbon at the cathode   ☐

3   True or false?

   Aluminium forms by a chemical reaction called reduction.

4   Galvanised iron is iron covered in:

   a   gold   ☐

   b   plutonium   ☐

   c   carbon   ☐

   d   zinc   ☐

5   Which is the negative electrode, the cathode or the anode?

Nitrogen and fertilisers

You know from biology that plants (producers) make all the food energy found in all living things. To do this they must have a source of usable nitrogen. Where do they get it?

The air is 78 per cent nitrogen (N_2) but plants cannot use this directly. To boost productivity scientists have developed industrial processes to produce fertilisers containing nitrogen.

The Haber process

This combines nitrogen gas (N_2) with hydrogen gas (H_2), as shown in this equation:

$$N_2 + 3H_2 \rightleftharpoons 2NH_3$$

These steps are also included to make the process as efficient as possible:

- a high pressure (200 atmospheres)
- a temperature of 450°C
- the presence of iron, as a catalyst
- three parts hydrogen to one part nitrogen.

The production of nitric acid from ammonia

This is necessary to make the fertiliser ammonium nitrate.

- ammonia + oxygen $\Rightarrow$ nitrogen monoxide + water
- nitrogen monoxide + water + oxygen $\Rightarrow$ nitric acid
- nitric acid + ammonia $\Rightarrow$ ammonium nitrate

Overuse of fertilisers

If nitrates get into water then the following often happens:

nitrates $\Rightarrow$ cause photosynthesising algae (bacteria) to multiply rapidly (called an algal bloom) $\Rightarrow$ many then die $\Rightarrow$ decomposer bacteria multiply $\Rightarrow$ oxygen levels drop (because the decomposers respire aerobically) $\Rightarrow$ the low oxygen levels cause death of fish

The whole process is called **eutrophication** – which means the water is too rich in nutrients.

GRADE BOOSTER

The most common mistake with eutrophication is to say the algae remove oxygen from the water. This cannot be true – they photosynthesise and add oxygen!

Question Bank 47

1 Atoms of which elements combine in the Haber process?

   a hydrogen and nickel ☐

   b hydrogen and nitrogen ☐

   c hyrlrogen and neon ☐

   d hydrogen and sodium ☐

2 Which metal is used as a catalyst in the Haber process?

3 Which combination of factors makes the Haber process more efficient?

   a a high pressure (200 atmospheres) and a temperature of 450°C ☐

   b a high pressure (200 atmospheres) and a low temperature of 50°C ☐

   c a low pressure (one atmosphere) and a temperature of 450°C ☐

   d a low pressure (one atmosphere) and a temperature of 50°C ☐

4 In this equation, what is the ratio of hydrogen to nitrogen?

$$N_2 + 3H_2 \rightleftharpoons 2NH_3$$

   a 1N : 3H ☐

   b 2N : 3H ☐

   c 3N : 2N ☐

   d 1N : 1H ☐

5 True or false?

Photosynthesising algae directly cause a drop in oxygen levels in water
polluted with nitrates.

Chemical equations

> This is quite easy provided you have some fundamentals clear in your mind. An equation in chemistry is the same as in maths – things have to balance.

In maths $5 + 3 = 8$. In chemistry $NaOH + HCl \Rightarrow NaCl + H_2O$. The atoms are conserved in the reaction – the same ones, in the same numbers, must be on the left and right. The most common mistakes happen when students do not remember what the numbers mean.

Take a look at these examples:

H_2O	two hydrogens but only one oxygen
H_2O_2	two hydrogens and two oxygens
NH_4NO_3	four hydrogens, three oxygens and two nitrogens
$2NO$	two molecules of NO
$Ca(OH)_2$	one calcium and two OH groups

Let's do a count of atoms in the reaction $NaOH + HCl \Rightarrow NaCl + H_2O$.

Reactants	Atoms present	Products	Atoms present
NaOH	Na O H	NaCl	Na Cl
HCl	H Cl	H_2O	2H O
Totals	1 Na, 1 O, 2 H, 1 Cl	**Totals**	1 Na, 1 O, 2 H, 1 Cl

Here are two more examples:

1 Determine the equation for the reaction in which H_2 and Cl_2 combine to form HCl. There are 2H and 2Cl in the reactants, so the equation is balanced like this:

$$H_2 + Cl_2 \Rightarrow 2HCl$$

2 Balance the equation for the reaction of Mg and HCl to produce $MgCl_2$ and H_2 We are short of a Cl and an H in the products, so:

$$Mg + 2HCl \Rightarrow MgCl_2 + H_2$$

Note: You cannot invent the chemistry – you have to know that Mg forms two bonds and Cl only one.

GRADE BOOSTER

The presence of equal number of atoms on each side of the equation is called the *law of conservation of mass*. Atoms cannot be made or destroyed during a chemical reaction.

Question Bank 48

1 Which of these is the proper way to show two hydrogen (H) atoms
  in a molecule?

   a   2H

   b H_2

   c H^2

   d ^2H

2 How many atoms of each of these elements are present in $Ca(OH)_2$?

   a   one Ca, two O, two H

   b   one Ca, two O, one H

   c   two Ca, two O, two H

   d   one Ca, one O, two H

3 Which of these equations is balanced?

   a $H + Cl_2 \Rightarrow 2HCl$

   b $H_2 + Cl \Rightarrow HCl$

   c $H_2 + Cl_2 \Rightarrow H_2Cl$

   d $H_2 + Cl_2 \Rightarrow 2HCl$

4 True or false?

   We can conclude from the formula $MgCl_2$ that one magnesium atom forms one
   bond with a chlorine atom.

5 $(OH)_2$ means:

   a   two OH groups

   b   two H and one O

   c   OH squared

   d   OH joined to two other atoms

Relative atomic mass

Separate atoms are too light to weigh, but chemists can compare how heavy different atoms are – some have relatively more mass than others.

The mass of an element depends upon how many particles are in the nucleus. Carbon has six protons and six neutrons; whereas oxygen has eight protons and eight neutrons.

Relative atomic mass (A_r)

All the masses quoted in the periodic table are relative to each other. So magnesium, with an atomic mass of 24, has twice the mass of carbon with a mass of 12 – in relative terms magnesium has twice the mass of carbon.

Here is a table showing the relative masses of the atoms of three elements.

Element	Nucleus contains	Relative atomic mass (A_r)
Hydrogen	1 proton, no neutrons	1
Helium	2 protons and 2 neutrons	4
Magnesium	12 protons and 12 neutrons	24

Note: Electron mass is so small it is ignored, and protons and neutrons are assumed to have equal mass.

Relative formula mass (M_r) is easy to understand provided you have grasped the A_r idea. You just add up the masses of all the atoms.

This table shows some chemical formulae and how to calculate M_r.

Formula	A_r values (see periodic table)	Total M_r value
H_2O	H = 1, O = 16	$2 \times 1 + 16 = 18$
$Ca(OH)_2$	Ca = 40, O = 16, H = 1	$40 + (2 \times (16 + 1)) = 74$
$MgCl_2$	Mg = 24, Cl = 35.5	$24 + (2 \times 35.5) = 95$

GRADE BOOSTER

All of the A_r values are based upon multiples of one-twelfth of the mass of a carbon-12 atom.

Question Bank 49

Given the values for A_r in the following table, calculate the M_r (relative formula mass) for each of the molecules listed below.

Element	A_r (relative atomic mass)
H	1
Cl	35.5
O	16
Mg	24
Ca	40

1 $Ca(OH)_2$

2 MgO

3 O_2

4 Cl_2

5 H_2O_2

The atmosphere and oceans

From your knowledge of biology you probably know that gases are being continuously added to and removed from the atmosphere. For example, respiration adds carbon dioxide and removes oxygen.

The current proportions of gases in the atmosphere remain approximately constant (see pie chart), but in the distant past the gases and their proportions were very different.

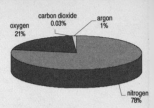

So what happened in the past? Study this table.

Billions of years ago (approx.)	Key events and changes in the atmosphere
4.5	The Earth is a ball of molten rock. Light gases (helium and hydrogen) escape gravity and enter space.
4	Volcanoes emit carbon dioxide and water and some methane and ammonia. This was the atmosphere about 4 billion years ago.
4–3	Water condenses as the Earth's crust cools – oceans form.
2–3	Nitrifying and denitrifying bacteria convert ammonia to nitrate and nitrates to nitrogen gas (N_2).
2–3	Most of the carbon dioxide is removed by photosynthesis (ultimately forming fossil fuels) or stored as carbonates in the sea (forming limestone – chalk). Ammonia and methane are lost as they react with oxygen.
1–2	Photosynthesising bacteria add poisonous oxygen – a very reactive gas that kills most microbes.
0–1	Ozone layer forms – blocking out UV radiation.
0–Present	Human activity causing a rise in carbon dioxide, due to burning fossil fuels and deforestation.

GRADE BOOSTER

Remember that you have studied most of these processes in biology – you only have to learn them once. Cross-refer between subjects.

Question Bank 50

1 Carbon dioxide is removed from the atmosphere by:

   a respiration ☐

   b combustion ☐

   c photosynthesis ☐

   d decomposition ☐

2 Volcanoes added which combination of gases to the early atmosphere?

   a oxygen, carbon dioxide and methane ☐

   b ammonia, carbon dioxide and methane ☐

   c nitrogen, oxygen and argon ☐

   d helium, hydrogen and carbon dioxide ☐

3 Ozone blocks out which form of radiation?

4 Two reasons are given for a rise in carbon dioxide levels in the atmosphere.
   One was deforestation; what was the other?

5 True or false?

   The oceans formed by condensation of water vapour from volcanoes.

Periodic table 1

The key to understanding the periodic table is how it's put together. By looking at the history of the table you can see what the key points are.

Putting the table together involved a process of detection where facts were gradually gathered until firm conclusions could be made.

Here are the main points in historical order.

By the mid-19th century chemists knew:

■ that atoms existed   ■ the relative mass of many atoms

■ that elements were in groups, based on their properties.

Dobereiner (1829) suggested the idea of 'triads' – elements grouped in threes (e.g. Li, Na, K).

The first periodic table was drawn by John Newlands in 1864.

H	Li	Be	B	C	N	O
F	Na	Mg	Al	Si	P	S
Cl	K	Ca				

■ Newlands put the elements in order of atomic mass.

■ If you count along seven elements (from any other), you get to an element with similarities.

■ This worked well for lighter elements, but heavier ones like iron were not included.

Dmitri Mendeleev took this process further. He put the known elements in groups but also added undiscovered 'unknowns'. Here is an unknown that he described in 1869: 'Unknown – grey metal, white oxide, its chloride will boil at less than 100°C, 1 cm^3 will weigh 1.9 g.' Germanium – discovered in 1896.

The noble gases

These non-reactive gases were discovered later and put in a new eighth group. But argon had an atomic mass that did not fit neatly in the sequence.

Finally, Rutherford and Moseley put the elements in order of atomic number (proton number) rather than relative mass.

GRADE BOOSTER

It's the number of protons (= number of electrons) that determines an element's chemistry. Adding neutrons adds mass, but does not change the element.

Question Bank 51

1 Who suggested putting elements in threes (triads)?

   a Dobereiner ☐

   b Mendeleev ☐

   c Rutherford ☐

   d Newlands ☐

2 Who produced a table with just seven groups?

   a Dobereiner ☐

   b Mendeleev ☐

   c Rutherford ☐

   d Newlands ☐

3 Who put unknowns into the table?

   a Dobereiner ☐

   b Mendeleev ☐

   c Rutherford ☐

   d Newlands ☐

4 Who put the elements in order of atomic number?

   a Dobereiner ☐

   b Mendeleev ☐

   c Rutherford ☐

   d Newlands ☐

5 True or false?

   Increasing the number of neutrons increases the atomic number.

Periodic table 2

The periodic table is organised in two ways. Fix them in your mind.

Vertically the elements are in **groups** – each element in the group has similar properties. Horizontally they are in **periods**, organised by atomic number.

See the periodic table on page 194.

The similarities and differences in properties of elements within each group are understood from the electron structure of the atoms. Study this table of the first 20 elements.

Element	Atomic number	Electron shells and how they fill			
		1st	2nd	3rd	4th
Hydrogen	1	1			
Helium	2	2			
Lithium	**3**	**2**	**1**		
Beryllium	4	2	2		
Boron	5	2	3		
Carbon	6	2	4		
Nitrogen	7	2	5		
Oxygen	8	2	6		
Fluorine	9	2	7		
Neon	10	2	8		
Sodium	**11**	**2**	**8**	**1**	
Magnesium	12	2	8	2	
Aluminium	13	2	8	3	
Silicon	14	2	8	4	
Phosphorus	15	2	8	5	
Sulphur	16	2	8	6	
Chlorine	17	2	8	7	
Neon	18	2	8	8	
Potassium	**19**	**2**	**8**	**8**	**1**
Calcium	20	2	8	8	2

You can see that the numbers of electrons in the first three shells go up to 2, 8, 8 respectively. The first three shells can hold this many electrons, and are then full.

Those elements in bold are all in group 1 of the periodic table. Notice that they each have only one electron in their outer shell.

GRADE BOOSTER

It's the number of electrons in the *outer shell* that determines how an element reacts.

Question Bank 52

When the first three electron shells are full, you have this number pattern: 2, 8, 8.

Using the atomic numbers given below, work out the number of electrons in each shell. The first has been done for you.

Question	Element	Atomic number	Electron shells and how they fill			
			1st	2nd	3rd	4th
Example	Beryllium	4	2	2		
1	Boron	5				
2	Nitrogen	7				
3	Neon	10				
4	Aluminium	13				
5	Chlorine	17				

The transition elements

> *You may have been wondering what has happened to the large block of elements found in the middle of the periodic table. They are the **transition metals**, including iron and copper.*

In comparison to the alkali metals (e.g. sodium), the transition metals are much harder and stronger, but share some properties with metals of other groups.

They share these properties with the metals of group 1:

- good conductors of heat and electricity
- can be pulled and hammered into shape (the technical words are *ductile* and *malleable*).

They differ from group 1 metals, in that they:

- have high melting points (except for mercury)
- are hard, tough and strong
- are much less reactive, and corrode less easily with water and oxygen.

Their uses are very broad and rely upon their properties – see the table below.

Metal or alloy	Use	Property
Steel (alloy of iron and carbon)	Structural – car bodies, bridges, cables/chains	Tensile strength, toughness
Stainless steel (iron, carbon and nickel alloy)	Saucepans, 'chromium' parts of bicycles	As above and corrosion resistance
Copper	Electrical wires Water pipes	Conducts electricity Non-corrosive
Alloys of copper, tin and zinc	Coinage	Hard-wearing
Gold	Jewellery	Does not tarnish

Identifying transition metals – by colour

The following reactions give distinctive colours:

copper sulphate + sodium hydroxide $\Rightarrow$ copper hydroxide (**blue** ppt) + sodium sulphate

iron sulphate + sodium hydroxide $\Rightarrow$ iron hydroxide (**green** ppt) + sodium sulphate

iron chloride + sodium hydroxide $\Rightarrow$ iron hydroxide (**brown** ppt) + sodium chloride

GRADE BOOSTER

Remember – iron was also a vital catalyst in the Haber process.

Question Bank 53

1 Which combination of terms best distinguishes transition metals from group 1 metals?

   a   hard, more reactive, ductile

   b   malleable, soft, strong

   c   ductile, strong, hard

   d   ductile, malleable, soft

2 Coins are commonly made of alloys of which metals?

   a   copper, zinc, iron

   b   copper, tin, zinc

   c   plutonium, cadmium, sodium

   d   zinc, potassium, iron

3 Which metal hydroxide produces a blue colour?

4 Which metal is used as a catalyst in the Haber process?

5 Which metal is a good conductor and is used in electrical wires?

The alkali metals

These are the very reactive metals found in group 1 of the periodic table. You don't see them in nature because they combine so readily with other elements.

They are called alkali metals because when they react with water they form alkaline hydroxides.

Refer back to the table of the first 20 elements and their electron shells. Note the following points:

- each atom of lithium, sodium, potassium, etc., has only one electron in its outer shell
- if this electron is lost, the electron arrangement will be the same as an inert gas (stable)
- atoms in this group readily lose one electron, leaving an ion with a single positive charge; e.g. $Na \Rightarrow Na^+ + e^-$

The reactions and properties of the alkali metals are as follows.

In water they react vigorously – most reactive first:

potassium > sodium > lithium

In each case hydrogen gas (H_2) is produced, and with potassium it ignites due to the vigorous reaction.

$2Li + 2H_2O \Rightarrow 2LiOH + H_2$ (Just learn this once, and substitute Na or K for Li.)

Hydroxides (OH) are **alkaline** – they produce solutions with a pH of more than 7.

Here are some other key reactions and properties of these elements.

- They react with oxygen to form a white metal oxide, e.g. $4Na + O_2 \Rightarrow 2Na_2O$.
- Burning in oxygen produces flames that have these colours: – Li red; Na orange; K lilac.
- With chlorine they produce a white smoke – the metal chloride, e.g. NaCl.
- They are soft, and cut with a knife to reveal a shiny metallic surface.
- They conduct electricity well.

GRADE BOOSTER

Elements in group 1 become more reactive down the group, because the single electron is farther from the nucleus, is held less strongly, and is therefore lost more easily.

Question Bank 54

1 How many electrons do the alkali metals have in their outer shell?

   a 1 ☐

   b 3 ☐

   c 5 ☐

   d 2 ☐

2 Which of these alkali metals is most reactive: lithium, sodium or potassium?

3 Match the element with the flame colour produced when burnt in oxygen.

   Choose one colour for each, from this list: **lilac, red** or **orange**.

   a lithium ....

   b potassium ....

   c sodium ....

4 Yes or no?

   Do the alkali metals conduct electricity well?

5 Choose one correct statement from the following:

   Alkali metals

   a are in group 2 ☐

   b form acidic solutions in water ☐

   c become more reactive up the group ☐

   d become more reactive down the group ☐

The halogens

Fewer than one-quarter of the elements are non-metals. All the non-metals are found to the right of the periodic table. Group 7 elements, the halogens, are the most important to study.

Non-metals have low melting and boiling points, are brittle and crumbly.

- Each atom of fluorine, chlorine and bromine, etc., has seven electrons in its outer shell.
- If one electron is gained, the electron arrangement will be the same as an inert gas (stable).
- Atoms in this group readily gain one electron, leaving an ion with a single negative charge, e.g. $F + e^- \Rightarrow F^-$.

The reactions and properties of the halogens are as follows:

- They have coloured vapours (see table p194).
- They form molecules of pairs of atoms, e.g. Cl_2.
- They form ionic salts – e.g. sodium chloride (NaCl).
- They form molecular compounds with other non-metals.

Element	At room temp.	In water	In hexane
Fluorine	Pale yellow gas		
Chlorine	Yellow/green gas	Pale green, forms an acidic solution; universal indicator goes red	Colourless
Bromine	Brown volatile liquid	Orange, weakly acidic	Orange
Iodine	Grey solid	Very weak acid	Purple

Reaction with iron

Chlorine forms iron chloride (a brown solid); bromine forms iron bromide; and so on. These are salts – halogen means 'salt producer'.

$2Fe(s) + 3Cl_2 \Rightarrow 2FeCl_3(s)$

GRADE BOOSTER

Elements in group 7 become more reactive up the group, because the shell that needs a single electron is closer to the nucleus if the atom is smaller. The nucleus has a stronger attraction for an electron with fluorine than with chlorine, and so on.

Question Bank 55

1 True or false?

   Halogens are in group 7.

2 Which of these statements is correct?

   a Halogens are metals and are found to the right of the periodic table. ☐

   b Halogens are non-metals and are found to the right of the periodic table. ☐

   c Halogens are metals and are found to the left of the periodic table. ☐

   d Halogens are non-metals and are found to the left of the periodic table. ☐

3 How many electrons are found in the outer shells of fluorine, chlorine and bromine?

4 Which halogen forms a yellow/green gas?

5 For group 7 elements, reactivity increases up the group. Which statement correctly explains why?

   a The shell that needs a single electron is closer to the nucleus if the atom is smaller. ☐

   b The shell that needs a single electron is farther from the nucleus if the atom is smaller. ☐

   c The shell that loses a single electron is closer to the nucleus if the atom is larger. ☐

   d The shell that loses a single electron is farther from the nucleus if the atom is larger. ☐

The noble gases

These gases took a long time to discover as they hardly ever combine with other elements in reactions. Without evidence of reactions, they were hard to identify.

In reactions, atoms exchange electrons (or share them). The noble gases are very stable as atoms because their outer shells are full.

Refer to the other pages about electron shells, and read these points:

■ Both neon and argon have eight electrons in their outer shells, and helium has two (all outer shells are full).

■ If one electron is gained or lost, the electron arrangement will not be that of an noble gas (stable).

All elements in this group share these characteristics:

■ They are very unreactive.

■ They exist as single atoms.

■ They are used as inert gases in filament lamps and electrical discharge tubes.

■ Helium is less dense than air and is used in balloons.

The uses of noble gases are summarised in this table.

Element		Boiling pt °C	Uses	Reason for use
Helium	He	−270	Balloons and airships	Lighter than air and does not ignite!
Neon	Ne	−249	The gas in advertising tubes	Glows red when electricity passes through
Argon	Ar	−189	The gas in light bulbs and an inert atmosphere for welding	Does not react with a red-hot filament or with a welding flame
Krypton and Xenon	Xe Kr	−157 −112	Lighthouse and projector bulbs	Will not react with a hot filament

GRADE BOOSTER

The electron shells of the noble gases all have filled outer shells – 2 (He), 8 (Ne), 8 (Ar).

Question Bank 56

1 True or false?

The noble gases are very stable because their outer shell is full.

2 True or false?

If the outer shell is full, atoms tend to lose or gain electrons.

3 Which of these combinations is true of the noble gases?

   a They are very reactive and they exist as single atoms. ☐

   b They are very unreactive and they do not exist as single atoms. ☐

   c They are very unreactive and they exist as single atoms. ☐

   d They are very reactive and they do not exist as single atoms. ☐

4 Which noble gas glows red when electricity is passed through it?

5 True or false?

Helium is used for airships and balloons because it is denser than air.

Rates of reaction 1

> This is one of the topics where you use your understanding more than just your knowledge. Understanding the graphs and diagrams is the key.

The rate of a reaction is how fast it happens. A fast reaction takes less time than a slow one, as shown in this equation:

Rate of reaction $\alpha \ \dfrac{1}{\text{time}}$

This looks difficult at first, but if you put numbers into the equation it makes sense.

Time for reaction to happen (seconds)	Calculate the rate, ^{1}/time	The rate of reaction (s^{-1})
2	$1 \div 2 = 0.5$	0.5
1	$1 \div 1 = 1.0$	1.0
0.5	$1 \div 0.5 = 2.0$	2.0
0.25	$1 \div 0.25 = 4.0$	4.0

So, the shorter the time it takes, the faster the rate.

Let's consider examples of slow and quick reactions.

Slow. Many statues are made of marble (calcium carbonate). When acid rain falls on them, this happens:

calcium carbonate + sulphuric acid $\Rightarrow$ calcium sulphate + carbon dioxide

Clearly, this takes a long time, but the statue is gradually worn away.

Fast. When a lighted splint is placed in a tube of hydrogen (H_2), a reaction occurs with oxygen and a squeaky pop is heard. This takes a fraction of a second.

The rates of reactions are measured by determining:

■ how fast the reactants are used up

■ or how fast the product(s) are formed.

GRADE BOOSTER

If you're struggling with rates in an examination, put numbers into the equation Rate $\alpha \ \dfrac{1}{\text{time}}$ to see how times convert to rates.

Question Bank 57

1 If a reaction takes 5 seconds, using rate = 1 ÷ time, the rate is:

  a 2

  b 50

  c 0.5

  d 0.2

2 Complete the equation

calcium carbonate + sulphuric acid ⇒ calcium sulphate + ...

....

3 Fill in the blank.

Hydrogen reacts with .... giving a squeaky pop.

4 Which of the following shows how rates of reaction are measured?

  a how quickly the reactants form

  b how fast the products are used up

  c how fast reactants are used up

  d how quickly the products become reactants

5 Which formula shows the relationship between rate and time?

  a Rate $\propto \dfrac{1}{\text{time}}$

  b Rate $\propto$ time

  c Rate $\propto \dfrac{1}{(\text{time})^2}$

  d Rate $\propto$ time^2

Rates of reaction 2

> *This topic is about how to get results to measure a rate of reaction and how to read the graph produced. Graphs are a great favourite of examiners – they are a good test of understanding.*

Remember, the rate of reaction is the speed it happens and can be measured by timing the formation of product (or loss of reactants).

This equipment is a good way of measuring a rate of reaction where the product is a gas.

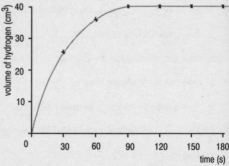

acid
magnesium ribbon

A classic reaction for this equipment is magnesium ribbon in dilute hydrochloric acid:

$$Mg(s) + 2HCl(aq) \Rightarrow MgCl_2(aq) + H_2(g)$$

The gas is collected in the syringe and this graph is drawn.

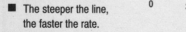

How do we read the graph?

Start at the far left and ask yourself what is happening on the y-axis.

- The steeper the line, the faster the rate.

- Where it levels off, no new gas is produced so the reaction has stopped. It has stopped because either there is no hydrochloric acid left or no more magnesium.

GRADE BOOSTER

Before you start to read the graph make sure you've studied the axes carefully – the most common error is to assume it is always time on the x-axis.

Question Bank 58

1 From this equation, state which molecule is collected by the syringe.

   $Mg(s) + 2HCl(aq) \Rightarrow MgCl_2(aq) + H_2(g)$

2 If the graph (on opposite page) has a steeper line, it means the rate is:

   a constant

   b slowing

   c quicker

   d zero

3 If the graph (on opposite page) levels out, this means the rate is:

   a constant

   b slowing

   c quicker

   d zero

4 When magnesium reacts with acid, why does the reaction eventually stop?

   a There is too much magnesium.

   b The acid has not reacted with the magnesium.

   c The magnesium may have all reacted.

   d There is too much acid.

5 True or false?

   All graphs have time on the x-axis.

Rates of reaction 3

You should have appreciated by now that rates of reaction vary. In industry, rates need to be as high as possible for commercial (cost) reasons.

There are several factors that can increase the rate of reaction. Rates can be maximised by using all or a combination of the following:

- increasing the temperature
- increasing the concentration of reactants, or increasing the pressure of a gas
- increasing the surface area (of a solid reactant)
- adding a catalyst.

The effect of increasing temperature

This is termed **kinetic theory**.

▼ Increases in temperature
▼ Increase the amount of heat
▼ More heat and particles have more kinetic energy (move more)
▼ This increases the probability of collisions between reactants
= faster rate of reaction

Note: Not all collisions result in a reaction. For a reaction to occur, there must be a minimum **activation energy**. Study this graph.

Key points to note:

- A certain amount of energy is put in to start the reaction (activation energy).
- With this graph the products have less energy than the reactants, so it is an **exothermic** reaction.

- The dashed line shows the effect of adding a catalyst – less activation energy is needed.

GRADE BOOSTER

Remember – *catalysts* speed up reactions by lowering the activation energy. Only small amounts of catalyst are needed because they are not used up in the reaction – they continue to work.

Question Bank 59

1 Complete this sentence using these terms:
kinetic, **collisions**, **temperature**.

With increasing **a** .... there is more heat, and particles have

more **b** .... energy. This increases the chance of

c .... happening.

2 What is the term given to the energy that has to be put in to start a reaction?

   a activation energy   ☐

   b acquisitive energy   ☐

   c aquitaine energy   ☐

   d acidic energy   ☐

3 True or false?

If the products have less energy than the reactants, the reaction is exothermic.

4 True or false?

A catalyst lowers the activation energy needed.

5 Which of these will **not** increase the rate of reaction?

   a increasing the temperature   ☐

   b increasing the concentration of reactants   ☐

   c adding a catalyst   ☐

   d decreasing the surface area of a solid   ☐

Enzymes 1

You will have studied enzymes in biology, where they seem to come up in most topics. In chemistry we need to consider their uses in industry.

Enzymes are protein molecules obtained from living cells. They are proteins. The catalysts usually mentioned in chemistry are metals – iron, platinum, etc.

So why use enzymes, rather than metal catalysts?

- They work at normal temperatures, 40°C (just warm) is typical.
- Low temperatures mean a saving on heating (compare to Haber process at 450°C).
- They are highly specific – they work on only one molecule (substrate).
- Being natural they do not harm the environment (biodegradable).

The difficulty of using enzymes or cells containing them (e.g. yeast) include:

- the risk of contamination with other microorganisms
- the need to maintain the pH within narrow limits (enzymes denature and organisms may die)
- the need to remove toxic waste products
- maintaining a constant supply of substrates ('food')
- keeping the temperature within narrow limits.

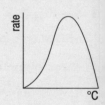

Key points on graph:

- low temperatures = lack of collisions
- optimum temperature gives the best yield
- high temperatures denature enzymes and kill microbes.

GRADE BOOSTER

Cross-refer to enzymes in biology. There's no point in learning the same material twice.

Question Bank 60

1 Are enzymes made of metal or protein?

2 Which of these statements is true of enzymes?

   a They work best at 450°C. ☐

   b They work well in all pH conditions. ☐

   c Their optimum temperature is the highest temperature at which
      they work. ☐

   d Their optimum temperature is the temperature at which they
      work best. ☐

3 True or false?

   Enzymes cannot be used in the Haber process.

4 Add these words to complete the sentence:
   enzymes, **denatured**, **catalysts**.

   Living cells contain protein **a** .... called **b** ....
   They work within a narrow pH range. If this pH range is exceeded they will be
   c ....

5 Which of these statements is true?

   a Enzymes are highly specific and therefore work at only one pH. ☐

   b Enzymes are highly specific and therefore work at only
      one temperature. ☐

   c Enzymes are highly specific and therefore only work on
      one substrate. ☐

   d Enzymes are highly specific and therefore only work in cells. ☐

Enzymes 2

You should have a good grasp of the basics of enzymes from biology and chemistry; but what uses do they have in industry?

Enzymes, or the microbes that contain them, can, under carefully controlled conditions, produce a single product molecule at high rates at warm temperatures.

Here are some of their uses:

- Biological detergents contain lipases and proteases to digest fat and protein respectively. The washing machine has to be run on a cool cycle, though.

- In the production of some baby foods, proteases are used to pre-digest the food.

- Starch is a very cheap carbohydrate (e.g. from maize); carbohydrase enzymes produce a more valuable product – sugar.

- Cheap sucrose (table sugar from sugar cane) is converted to glucose and fructose by the enzyme invertase.

- Hard-centred chocolates are changed into soft-centred by injection of invertase (converts sucrose to glucose + fructose).

- The enzyme systems of yeast are used to make ethanol (drinking alcohol) and to produce carbon dioxide to make bread rise.

- Other microbes are used to convert milk lactose to lactic acid to make yoghurt.

Testing for carbon dioxide

Carbon dioxide gas is bubbled through limewater (calcium hydroxide), causing a milky precipitate of calcium carbonate to form:

$$Ca(OH)_2(aq) + CO_2(g) \Rightarrow CaCO_3(s) + H_2O(l)$$

GRADE BOOSTER

There's a limit to what an examiner can ask you in examinations – any question on the use of enzymes is likely to ask for just two examples of their use in industry; make sure you learn at least two.

Question Bank 61

1 True or false?

With biological detergents (containing enzymes) the washing cycle is cool, to prevent enzymes denaturing.

2 Choose the correct answer from the following:

a Lipase digests protein and fat. ☐

b Protease digests fat and protein. ☐

c Lipase digests protein. ☐

d Protease digests protein. ☐

3 What is tested for by the limewater test?

4 Hard-centred sweets can be softened by injecting:

a inverted ☐

b glucose ☐

c invertase ☐

d glucase ☐

5 What chemical forms the milky precipitate with the limewater test?

Types of chemical reaction

This topic pulls together ideas from all over chemistry. It will help you see common themes that run through the course.

Chemists show what has happened in word or symbol equations – on one side are the reactants and on the other the products.

The basic types of reaction are shown in this table.

Type of reaction	Definition	Example
Thermal decomposition	Heat splits up a compound	Cracking: longer hydrocarbons split to form ethene
Neutralisation	An acid and base (or alkali) react to form salt and water	$KOH + HCl \Rightarrow KCl + H_2O$
Displacement	A more reactive element will displace a less reactive one	$Fe + CuSO_4 \Rightarrow FeSO_4 + Cu$ The iron (Fe) displaces the copper (Cu)
Electrolysis	The splitting of an electrolyte (molten or a solution) by electricity	Aluminium oxide is split, with aluminium forming at the cathode and oxygen at the anode
Oxidation	A reaction in which an oxygen is added or a hydrogen lost	Magnesium gains oxygen when burned $2Mg + O_2 \Rightarrow 2MgO$
Reduction	A reaction in which a hydrogen is added or an oxygen lost	Copper oxide reduced in hydrogen gas $CuO + H_2 \Rightarrow Cu + H_2O$
Exothermic	A reaction where energy is lost to the surroundings – as energy released in bond formation exceeds energy needed to break bonds	Combustion reactions $CH_4 + 2O_2 \Rightarrow CO_2 + 2H_2O$ Methane burning
Endothermic	The opposite of exothermic	Calcium chloride + sodium carbonate: there is a temperature drop
Reversible	A reaction that can go backwards or forwards	$N_2 + 3H_2 \rightleftharpoons 2NH_3$

GRADE BOOSTER

Remember – reactions involve the breaking and forming of bonds. Energy needs to be supplied to break bonds, and energy is released when bonds form.

Question Bank 62

1 One example of thermal decomposition is:

    a quaking ☐

    b crunching ☐

    c creaking ☐

    d cracking ☐

2 Based upon the definition given, which one of these reactions is an example of oxidation?

    a $2Mg + O_2 \Rightarrow 2MgO$ ☐

    b $CuO + H_2 \Rightarrow Cu + H_2O$ ☐

    c $KOH + HCl \Rightarrow KCl + H_2O$ ☐

    d $Fe + CuSO_4 \Rightarrow FeSO_4 + Cu$ ☐

3 True or false?

Endothermic reactions always add heat to the environment.

4 Aluminium oxide is split, with aluminium forming at the cathode and oxygen at the anode. This is an example of:

    a a reversible reaction ☐

    b displacement ☐

    c electrolysis ☐

    d neutralisation ☐

5 True or false?

Energy is needed to break bonds.

Series and parallel circuits

This is a good example of a topic where there are different rules that apply to two situations. Take care to learn the details.

Current is the flow of electric charge. **Voltage** (or potential difference) gives a measure of the energy transfer form a source (e.g. battery) to a component (e.g. bulb).

Current and voltage

Measuring	Unit	Instrument used	How instrument is connected
Current	A – Amp	Ammeter	In series – measures the current passing through
Voltage	V – Volt	Voltmeter	In parallel with (across) components. To measure the energy transfer

Two key points:

1 The current transfers energy from the energy source (e.g. mains) to the component.
2 As current passes through an energy source, energy is transferred to it.

Here are two simple circuits, series and parallel.

Series

■ In a series circuit the current follows one path.
■ The current is the same at all points.
■ The sum of the voltages across each component equals the voltage across the batteries.

Parallel

■ The current can follow more than one path – it splits and then rejoins.
■ The current passing into a junction equals the current passing out.
■ Components in parallel have the same voltage.

GRADE BOOSTER

Remember – houses are wired in parallel to allow individual lights to be switched on and off.

Question Bank 63

1 The letter symbolising the unit for current is:

  a C ☐

  b A ☐

  c T ☐

  d S ☐

2 Which of these is the correct set-up for ammeters and voltmeters?

  a Ammeters are connected in series, voltmeters in parallel. ☐

  b Ammeters are connected in parallel, voltmeters in series. ☐

  c Ammeters and voltmeters are connected in series. ☐

  d Ammeters and voltmeters are connected in parallel. ☐

3 True or false?

The current transfers energy to components.

4 If the voltage across a battery is 6V, then two bulbs in series each have a voltage of:

  a 12V ☐

  b 4V ☐

  c 3V ☐

  d 0.5V ☐

5 If the voltage across a battery is 6V, then two bulbs in parallel each have a voltage of:

  a 12V ☐

  b 6V ☐

  c 3V ☐

  d 0.5V ☐

Current and resistance

It helps to build simple models in your head to understand things. Think of resistance as friction reducing the current flowing.

Resistance is a measure of the opposition to a current. The larger the resistance, the less current passes (assumes voltage is constant).

■ The relationship is shown by this formula:

$V = I \times R$ (or $I = V \div R$ or $R = V \div I$)

■ Resistance is measured in ohms; symbol Ω.

In your home the voltage is fixed at 230 V, so inserting into the equation we can calculate current (I) as follows:

If $R = 10\,\Omega$, then $I = {}^{230}\!/_{10} = 23\,A$

■ The rule for the way resistors behave is given as:

the current (at constant temperature) is proportional to the voltage across the resistor. Or in graph form:

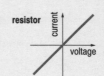

But this rule does not always apply, as shown by these two graphs:

This shows the effect on resistance of a lamp filament. As it gets hotter, the resistance increases.

A **diode** only allows a current to flow one way – resistance is very high the other way.

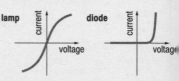

Two uses are made of this variation in resistance:

■ a **light-dependent resistor** (LDR) has decreased resistance with increases in light levels – it can be used to switch on a light when it gets dark

■ a **thermistor**'s resistance decreases with increases in temperature – it can be used to trigger a fire alarm.

GRADE BOOSTER

Assuming a domestic supply of 230 V, find out the resistance of different appliances and calculate the current flowing – or make up values to practise.

Question Bank 64

1 Which of these equations is wrong?

   a $V = IR$ ☐

   b $I = V \div R$ ☐

   c $R = V \div I$ ☐

   d $V = I \div R$ ☐

2 Assuming a voltage of 20V and a resistance of 2Ω, the current is:

   a 10A ☐

   b 20A ☐

   c 40A ☐

   d 12A ☐

3 True or false?

   As the temperature of a lamp filament increases, the resistance decreases.

4 True or false?

   In a diode, the current can only flow one way.

5 Add either **increases** or **decreases** to complete the following sentence.

   A thermistor's resistance decreases with .... in temperature.

Electrical appliances and costs

> *Electricity is a very useful source of energy in the home (and industry) as it can readily be transferred as heat, light, sound or movement.*

The amount of energy transferred to an appliance depends upon how fast it transfers energy (= power) and how long it is on.

■ The equation is:

energy transferred = power × time

Always starting with electrical energy, here are some examples:

Lawnmower $\Rightarrow$ kinetic energy

Kettle $\Rightarrow$ heat energy

Light bulb $\Rightarrow$ light energy + heat energy

Radio $\Rightarrow$ sound energy

How much will it cost?

This depends upon the energy transferred (measured in **kilowatt hours**, kWh)

= power (kW) × time (h)

Note: 1 watt is one joule of energy transferred in 1 second.

■ If an appliance needs 1kW of energy to run and you have it on for one hour, it will have used up 1kWh (also called a Unit, U).

The total cost is number of Units × cost per Unit. If we assume 7p per Unit, then this table gives two examples.

Appliance	kW needed	Time (h)	Total cost
Light bulb	0.1 (=100W)	30 mins/0.5 hour	$0.1 \times 0.5 \times 7 = 0.35$p
Iron	0.9	60 mins/1 hour	$0.9 \times 1 \times 7 = 6.3$p
Shower	10	30mins/0.5 hour	$10 \times 0.5 \times 7 = 35$p

GRADE BOOSTER

Make up your own examples to find out how much things cost to run. Practise the maths and you'll get better.

Question Bank 65

1 Electricity can transfer energy in many forms. Which one is **not** correct?

   a Sound ☐

   b Light ☐

   c Heat ☐

   d Radioactivity ☐

2 True or false?

   Energy transferred is calculated as power ÷ time.

3 True or false?

   One kilowatt hour is the energy transferred to a 1 kW appliance if it is left on for an hour.

4 Assuming electricity costs 7p per Unit (U), how much will a 100 W lamp on for one hour cost?

5 If an iron costs 3.5 p to run for 30 minutes, its wattage is ....

Mains electricity and safety

This is one of those topics where you really do learn something that you can use for the rest of your life!

To be safe, you are either kept separate from electricity by non-conducting materials, or fuses cut the circuit.

Starting from outside the house, your electricity arrives as an alternating current (a.c.) at 230V, with a frequency of 50Hz – which means the current switches backwards and forwards 50 times each second.

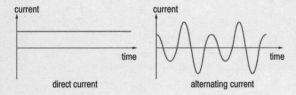

direct current   alternating current

The key safety features are as follows.

Feature	Safety considerations and features
Well-wired plugs	Blue to neutral, brown to live, yellow and green (if present) to earth. A tightened cable grip to prevent wires being pulled out. Intact plastic case and plastic wire on cable – for insulation.
Fuses and circuit-breakers	Fuses in appliances should have a value close to, but higher, than the current rating. If a short-circuit causes a larger than normal current to flow, the fuse melts, breaking the circuit. Circuit-breakers work more quickly and can be reset easily.
Earthing	If an appliance has a metal case, it must be earthed to prevent it becoming live. The earth wire is linked to the ground – by offering low resistance the current flows to earth.

GRADE BOOSTER

Find a way of remembering which wire is which in a plug. Here's one way: water has a *neutral* pH and appears *blue*. Trees are *live* and *brown*. The other one is the earth.

Question Bank 66

1   Match up the colour with the wires.

   Colour   **a** blue   **b** brown   **c** yellow/green

   Wire   **i** live   **ii** earth   **iii** neutral

2   If an appliance has a normal current of 11 A, which of these fuses should
    you use?

   a   13A   ☐

   b   11A   ☐

   c   3A   ☐

   d   110A   ☐

3   Add the missing words to complete this paragraph:
    earthed, **metal**, **resistance**, **ground**.

   If an appliance has a **a** .... case then it must be **b** ....
   to prevent it becoming live. The earth wire is linked to the **c** ....
   By offering low **d** .... the current flows into the ground.

4   True or false?
    A tight cable grip is needed in a plug to prevent the fuse falling out.

5   Circuit-breakers are more convenient because:

   a   They switch themselves back on.   ☐

   b   They can be reset easily.   ☐

   c   They just need a new fuse.   ☐

   d   They do not cause loss of power.   ☐

Electrical charge

*You've probably experienced a static shock. Rubbing some materials
against others creates surface charge, which may discharge as a spark.*

Where the charges are the same (+ and + or – and –), repulsion occurs. Opposite
charges attract.

The charges result from transfer of electrons (negative charge) from one material to
another. The one that gains electrons becomes negative, and the other positive.
Bearing this in mind, these uses are made of electrostatic charges.

Use	How they work
Photocopier	A copying plate is charged
	The image of a page is projected onto the plate
	Charge is lost where light strikes – reflected off white parts of the paper
	Black powder sticks where charge remains
	Paper is heated to fix the ink
Inkjet printer	Ink droplets are charged when they are squirted through a tiny nozzle
	The ink passes between two plates (of opposite charge)
	By increasing/decreasing the charge or reversing the charge on the plates, the droplets can be aimed
	Numerous directed drops form the image

Static electricity can be dangerous

- When people are rescued from the sea by helicopter crews, the rescuer
  touches the water first before grabbing the person in the sea. This discharges
  any static and prevents a shock causing the person in the sea to let go.

- When planes are refuelled, they are earthed. Without this, static discharge
  could ignite the fuel.

GRADE BOOSTER

Remember – a moving charge is called a *current*.

Question Bank 67

1 Which combination of charges will attract?

   a positive and negative ☐

   b positive and neutral ☐

   c positive and positive ☐

   d negative and negative ☐

2 What are transferred from one material to another to cause a build-up of charge?

   a neutrons ☐

   b electrons ☐

   c positrons ☐

   d protons ☐

3 Add the missing words to this description of a printer:
   opposite, **charged**, **image**, **reversing**.

   Ink droplets are **a** .... when they are squirted through a tiny nozzle.
   The ink passes between two plates of **b** .... charge.
   By **c** .... the charge on the plates, the droplets can be aimed.
   Numerous drops accumulate, forming an **d** ....

4 What is the missing word?

   Planes have to be .... before refuelling to prevent sparks igniting the fuel.

5 What is the missing word?

   A current is a moving ....

Distance–time and velocity–time graphs

If you find you're getting bogged down with equations and graphs, try to think of a real-life situation to understand – e.g. a car moving.

If an object is moving in a straight line then the distance it has travelled can be shown on a distance–time graph.

By reading up from the x-axis, you can see how far the person/car has moved.

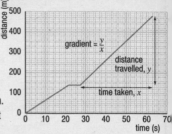

- In the first 15 seconds they moved 100 m.
- Between 22 and 27 seconds they did not move.

Dividing values of y by values of x you get the speed in metres per second.

- The steeper the graph, the faster they are going.

Reading speed–time graphs is similar.

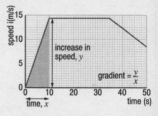

- In the first 10 seconds they went from 0 m/s (stationary) steadily up to 14.5 m/s – i.e. **accelerating**.
- Between 10 and 35 seconds the speed was fixed at 14.5 m/s – i.e. travelling at a **constant speed**.

By dividing values of y by values of x you get the increase in speed in m/s^2 = acceleration.

- The steeper the graph, the greater the acceleration.
- When the line drops they are slowing down – **decelerating**.

GRADE BOOSTER

Speed only tells you how fast an object is moving. *Velocity* also provides information about direction – a train travelling in different directions can be shown as positive and negative velocity.

Question Bank 68

1 At time 10 seconds we can read
   from the graph that the object is:

   a steadily accelerating ☐

   b going at constant speed ☐

   c travelling backwards ☐

   d travelling at about
         70 m per second ☐

   gradient = $\frac{y}{x}$

   distance travelled, y

   time taken, x

2 At time 25 seconds we can read from the graph that the object is:

   a steadily accelerating ☐

   b going at constant speed ☐

   c not moving ☐

   d travelling at about 140 m per second ☐

3 True or false?

   To calculate the speed in the first 15 seconds we have to divide 15 by the
   distance travelled.

4 True or false?

   In velocity–time graphs, if the line is horizontal, this means the velocity is
   constant.

5 True or false?

   In velocity–time graphs, if the graph line goes straight up, the object is moving
   at a constant velocity.

Forces, acceleration and friction

We experience forces all the time but often do not consider clearly what's happening – e.g. you're not falling through the floor because your downward force (weight) is opposed by the floor pushing up.

If forces are balanced, objects will not move, or if they are already moving they will do so at constant speed.

The effect of unbalanced forces depends upon their size and direction:

- A stationary object will move in the direction of the unbalanced force.
- If already moving in the direction of the force, the object speeds up.
- Conversely, if the force is in the opposite direction to the motion, the object slows.
- The greater the size of the unbalanced force, the faster it will speed up or slow down.

One other point to consider – the bigger the object's mass, the larger the force required to achieve a particular acceleration.

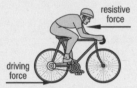

Friction

The resistive force is the friction of the air. Friction always opposes the object's movement in a particular direction. Study this table.

Force	Force	Which is larger	Effect
Resistive	Driving	Driving	Acceleration
Resistive	Driving	Resistive	Slow down
Resistive	Driving	Neither (same)	Constant velocity

GRADE BOOSTER

Remember – a cycle tyre needs friction on the road to provide the driving force – the tyre pushing on the road is shown pointing backwards; the road pushing on the tyre (driving force) points forwards.

Question Bank 69

1. A balloon is travelling in a straight line at constant speed. This suggests the forces are:

   a balanced ☐

   b greater in the direction of travel ☐

   c less in the direction of travel ☐

   d all downwards ☐

2. Add the missing words to complete these statements:
   increase, slows, unbalanced, size.

   The effect of an unbalanced force depends upon its **a** .... and direction.

   A stationary object will move in the direction of the **b** .... force.

   If already moving in the direction of a force, unbalanced forces will cause an **c** .... in speed.

   If a force is in the opposite direction to the motion, the object **d** ....

3. True or false?

   If the same force acts on two trolleys and one moves faster, we may assume the slower one is lighter.

4. True or false?

   If a car is slowing, the resistive force is greater than the driving force.

5. In which direction would an arrow point to show the driving force on a bicycle tyre?

Braking distances and falling objects

> *When you take your driving test, you'll be expected to remember some standard braking distances. This topic will help you understand.*

The greater the speed, the greater the braking force needed to stop it in a given distance; or the greater the distance needed to stop with a given braking force.

In practice it is the second statement that matters in emergencies, because we tend to brake as hard as possible!

But it is not just the brakes that matter – so does the mind. The overall stopping distance depends upon:

- the distance travelled before braking (**reaction time**)
- the distance travelled while braking.

You should note from this that:

- with double the speed, the thinking distance doubles
- with double the speed, the braking distance goes up by four times.

These distances assume the following:

30 mph
9 m   14 m

60 mph
18 m   56 m

thinking distance
braking distance

- the road conditions are good – dry, good visibility
- reactions are not affected by drugs/tiredness/inattention
- the vehicle's brakes work, and tyres are not worn.

Falling objects
1 Falling objects accelerate initially because gravitational force exceeds air friction.
2 Friction forces increase with increasing speed of falling.
3 These opposing forces balance, and a constant **terminal velocity** is achieved.

GRADE BOOSTER
Remember – a vehicle travelling at constant speed continues to need a driving force to overcome the balancing frictional forces.

Question Bank 70

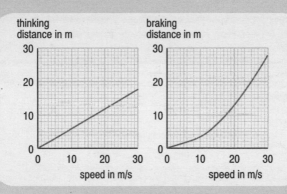

thinking distance in m / speed in m/s

braking distance in m / speed in m/s

1 From the graph, what is the thinking distance at a speed of 10 m/s?

2 At a speed of 10 m/s, what is the braking distance?

3 Calculate the stopping distance at a speed of 10 m/s (use both answers above).

4 Which of these factors will not affect the thinking distance?

   a a mobile phone ringing

   b alcohol in the bloodstream

   c an ABS braking system

   d tiredness

5 True or false?

If a ball is falling at constant speed, gravitational pull and air resistance (friction) will be equal.

Waves 1

Waves go from one place to another without any material travelling the distance. Waves transfer energy from a source to other places, without transferring matter. This happens by vibrations.

There are two types of wave: longitudinal and transverse, as shown by these two diagrams:

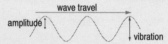

rarefaction
(stretch)

compression
(squash)

the vibrations in a logitudinal wave (above) and a transverse wave (below)

- **Longitudinal** waves include sound. They are best observed using springs. The disturbance is along the direction of the wave travel.
- **Transverse** waves include waves on the surface of water and light. They are best observed using ropes. The disturbance is across (transverse to) the direction of the wave travel.

Both types of wave have a frequency, wavelength and amplitude.

- The **frequency** is how many waves pass a point each second (or are generated by a source in a second).
- **Wavelength** is most simply the distance from crest to crest – or, more technically, the distance between a point on one disturbance and the same point on the next.
- **Amplitude** is the maximum disturbance.

This formula is used to calculate the wave speed:

Speed (v) = frequency (f) × wavelength (λ)

Note: If the frequency increases, the wavelength is shorter (assumes speed is constant).

GRADE BOOSTER

One of the most common errors is to assume that amplitude (in transverse waves) is the vertical distance from a crest to a trough – study the diagram carefully to avoid this mistake.

Question Bank 71

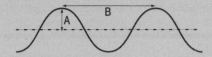

1 Which arrow shows the amplitude?

2 Which arrow shows the wavelength?

3 Which pair of statements describes the direction of the disturbance with transverse and longitudinal waves?

   a transverse in the direction of wave travel – longitudinal across ☐

   b longitudinal in the direction of wave travel – transverse across ☐

   c transverse backwards in the direction of wave travel – longitudinal forwards ☐

   d transverse sideways in the direction of wave travel – longitudinal has no disturbance ☐

4 The formula used to calculate wave speed (v) is:

   a $v = f \times \lambda$ ☐

   b $v = f \div \lambda$ ☐

   c $v = f + \lambda$ ☐

   d $v = f^2 \times \lambda$ ☐

5 True or false?

   If the frequency of a wave increases, its wavelength also increases.

Waves 2

We can all describe what we see waves doing on water, but it's important to use proper terms to explain the behaviour. Waves can bounce off, bend and spread out, or more technically: reflect, refract and diffract.

Reflection is shown in these three diagrams.

These are the key points to note:

incoming wave   reflected wave

reflected waves
incoming waves

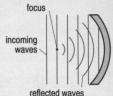
focus
incoming waves
reflected waves

- 1st diagram. The wave is reflected at the same angle – or the angle of incidence is equal to the angle of reflection.
- 2nd diagram. The reflected waves appear to have their source behind the surface – this origin is called the **image** (like images in mirrors).
- 3rd diagram. The parallel incoming waves are focused to a point – this is how satellite dishes work.

Refraction. When waves travel into a different material (or the same material with different density), they change direction.

- In more dense materials the speed drops and wavelength falls – but frequency is the same.

This diagram shows waves going from deeper to shallower water.

Notice that the wave regains its original angle and other characteristics.

Diffraction. If waves pass through a gap or past an obstacle, they spread out from the edges. This phenomenon explains why we can hear sounds in the 'shadow' of buildings.

GRADE BOOSTER

Particles can bounce off (reflect) but do not diffract – the fact that sound and light can both be diffracted shows that they have wave-like behaviour.

Question Bank 72

1   A wave is reflected off a flat surface at an angle of 30°. What was the angle of the incoming wave?

2   If a wave travels into a more dense material, which of these is true?

   a   The frequency increases and the wavelength decreases.   ☐

   b   The frequency remains the same and the wavelength decreases.   ☐

   c   The frequency increases and the wavelength remains the same.   ☐

   d   The frequency decreases and the wavelength increases.   ☐

3   True or false?

   Satellite dishes work by focusing waves at a point behind the dish.

4   When waves pass through a gap, they often spread out. This is called:

   a   reflection   ☐

   b   refraction   ☐

   c   rarefaction   ☐

   d   diffraction   ☐

5   True or false?

   Particles can be diffracted but not reflected.

Light as a wave

Unlike water waves, we do not see light as a wave – so why do we assume it is? Light behaves as if it is a wave: experiments on reflection, refraction and diffraction indicate that light behaves like a wave.

Reflection

You should note the following:

- the angle of incidence = the angle of reflection
- the image seen by an observer is behind the mirror, upright and the same size.

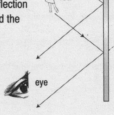

Refraction

If you look at a grill in the bottom of a swimming pool, it seems larger and closer to the surface than it is. This diagram shows why.

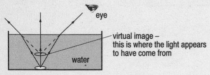

virtual image – this is where the light appears to have come from

When light in air enters a denser substance (glass, water) and leaves again, it behaves like this – note that the angle narrows between the light and the normal (vertical line) and spreads again as the light leaves.

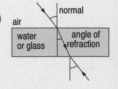

When light meets a boundary and goes to enter a material in which it will travel faster (glass to air), it can experience **total internal reflection**. For this to happen the angle relative to the normal must be greater than the critical angle (42°). This phenomenon has uses in optical fibres and the prisms in binoculars.

GRADE BOOSTER

When trying to understand mirrors it helps to realise that the brain puts the image behind the mirror – to make sense of the information received.

Question Bank 73

1 True or false?

Light is a longitudinal wave.

2 Which of these is true for reflections in plane mirrors?

  a The image seen is behind the mirror, upright and the same size. ☐

  b The image seen is in front of the mirror, upright and smaller. ☐

  c The image seen is behind the mirror, inverted and the same size. ☐

  d The image seen is behind the mirror, upright and smaller. ☐

3 When light enters a denser material the angle with the normal:

  a increases ☐

  b decreases ☐

  c stays the same ☐

  d disappears ☐

4 Fill in the blank.

For light passing from glass to air, for total internal reflection the angle relative to the normal must be more than .... degrees.

5 True or false?

Total internal reflection is used in simple light microscopes.

Electromagnetic spectrum 1

> *Remember that light, and all other forms of electromagnetic radiation, behave as transverse waves. Also if objects absorb radiation, they heat up.*

Visible light is just part of this spectrum. Our eyes have evolved to 'see' colours in this abundant white light.

Notice that the X-rays (and gamma) have shorter wavelengths and higher frequency.

frequency/Hz	10^{20}	10^{17}	10^{14}	10^{11}	10^{8}	10^{5}
	gamma rays	ultraviolet	infra-red		radio waves	
	X-rays		light	microwaves		
wavelength/m	10^{-12}	10^{-9}	10^{-6}	10^{-3}	1	10^{3}

All electromagnetic radiation, if absorbed, will heat materials. Different wavelengths are reflected, absorbed or transmitted differently by different substances.

Here is a table of uses of X-rays, gamma radiation and ultraviolet radiation. (There are more over the page.)

Form of radiation	Use
X-rays	Because of their ability to penetrate materials, images can be produced on X-ray film. Denser materials (bone and metal) absorb more of the radiation – bones appear white and breaks darker
Gamma	Due to its high energy and penetration it is used to: ■ kill harmful bacteria in food ■ sterilise surgical instruments ■ kill cancer cells (radiotherapy)
Ultraviolet	In sun beds – for suntans and some medical uses. For fluorescent lamps and security coding

Harmful effects

Each of the above can cause cancer by damaging the DNA of living cells. Damage is more likely in dividing cells, which is why cancer cells (which divide often) are killed by radiotherapy. Darker skins contain the chemical melanin, which prevents the radiation penetrating as far.

GRADE BOOSTER

Remember – all electromagnetic waves travel at the same speed in a vacuum: 300 million metres per second.

Question Bank 74

1 True or false?

Electromagnetic waves are transverse waves.

2 Which of these forms of radiation has the shortest wavelength?

a infra-red

b microwaves

c gamma

d UV

3 True or false?

Only infra-red radiation heats objects.

4 Which pair of statements is true for gamma radiation?

a It has a short wavelength and can be used to kill bacteria.

b It has a long wavelength and can be used to kill bacteria.

c It has a high frequency and can be used to obtain images of broken bones.

d It has a short wavelength and can be used for sun-tan beds.

5 X-radiation can cause cancers because it damages:

a proteins

b fats

c DNA

d carbohydrates

Electromagnetic spectrum 2

There are so many uses for the different forms of electromagnetic radiation that a question on this topic is quite likely.

■ Electromagnetic radiation is waves that transfer energy. The energy can be transferred very quickly – up to the speed of light.

This table continues the one on the previous page.

Form of radiation	Use
Light	For vision and photosynthesis In medicine, the total internal reflection in optical fibres is used in endoscopes (flexible tubes that can be inserted into people without the need for major surgery to see inside)
Infra-red	When absorbed by the skin it heats Also used to heat in grills, toasters and radiant heaters Communication, via optical fibres and in remote control of VCRs and TVs Infra-red scopes are used by the military and search and rescue to identify infra-red emissions from people
Microwave	Microwaves are strongly absorbed by water and are used in microwave cookers Because they penetrate the atmosphere well, they are used in satellite-to-ground communication and for mobile phones.
Radiowave	The longer wavelengths reflect off the Earth's upper atmosphere, allowing transmission of radio and TV programmes over huge distances

Digital vs. analogue signals

Both types of signal become distorted, but the distortion can be corrected with the on–off pattern of digital. Digital therefore allow for higher-quality transmission. Also, more information can be sent with digital signals.

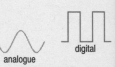

analogue   digital

GRADE BOOSTER

If absorbed, all forms of electromagnetic radiation can cause heating. A common error is to assume infra-red is heat – it just happens to be the radiation that is absorbed and heats our skin.

Question Bank 75

Match up the form of radiation with a use.

Form of radiation		Use
1 Radiowave	a	In medicine, the total internal reflection in optical fibres is used in endoscopes
2 Microwave	b	Used for remote control of VCRs and TVs
3 Infra-red	c	Because they penetrate the atmosphere well, they are used in satellite-to-ground communication and for mobile phones
4 Light	d	The longer wavelengths reflect off the Earth's upper atmosphere, allowing transmission of TV programmes over huge distances

5 True or false?

Analogue signals provide higher-quality transmission than digital.

The Earth's structure

*People have not penetrated far into the Earth, but we have knowledge of what lies within, partly through volcanic activity but also through **seismology**.*

Seismology is the detection and analysis of waves produced by earthquakes. Seismographs allow scientists to judge the state of the material through which the waves have passed.

Here are some key points:

- The overall density of the Earth is greater than the average density of materials in the crust (surface). The interior must therefore be constituted of denser material.
- The **mantle** is solid but has the property of a very slowly flowing liquid – this allows energy transfer from the centre to the surface.
- The **core** is made of nickel and iron, and the outer half is liquid.

Tectonics

The Earth's **lithosphere** (crust plus top part of the mantle) is made up of **tectonic plates** that move a few centimetres per year. The motion is driven by convection currents (see mantle above) produced by the heat generated by radioactive processes in the Earth.

Evidence to support tectonics includes:

- the fit that previously existed between South America and Africa (see map)
- the presence of very similar fossils now separated by oceans
- earthquakes and volcanic eruptions occur at plate boundaries.

GRADE BOOSTER

You may be asked to account for why Wegener's *theory of continental drift* (tectonics) was not originally accepted. Look it up in an encyclopedia.

Question Bank 76

1 True or false?

Seismology relies upon waves produced by earthquakes.

2 Which of these is **not** true of the Earth?

  a The overall density of the Earth is greater than the average density of materials in the crust (surface).

  b The mantle is solid but has the property of a very slowly flowing liquid.

  c The core is made of nickel and iron, and the outer half is liquid.

  d The interior is less dense than the crust.

3 The Earth's tectonic plates move by about how much per year?

  a a few metres

  b a few centimetres

  c not at all

  d a few kilometres

4 True or false?

It is the heat energy from radioactive processes that drives the tectonic plates.

5 Which of these is **not** evidence for tectonics?

  a The fit that previously existed between South America and Africa

  b The presence of very similar fossils now separated by oceans

  c Rocks laid down in sedimentary layers

  d Earthquakes and volcanic eruptions occur at plate boundaries

The solar system

You will have studied most of the key points in Key Stage 3. Here the focus is on what goes round the Sun or the Earth and why.

To maintain an orbit, objects must have a high speed and be attracted by the gravity of a larger body.

How gravity behaves

- If the distance from an object doubles, then the force of gravity drops by more than half. More precisely, doubling the distance reduces the gravity to one-quarter.
- The larger the mass of the objects involved, the bigger the gravitational force.

Different orbits

- The planets follow a slightly **elliptical** orbit (a squashed circle), with the Sun in about the middle. Pluto's orbit is the most elliptical.
- Comets follow a very elliptical orbit, which comes very close to the Sun. Vaporisation of ice allows them to be seen when near the Sun.
- The farther away an object is from the Sun, the longer it takes to orbit – it is travelling further and the lower gravitational force results in a slower speed.

Satellites

- To keep **communication** satellites at a fixed distance from the Earth, they must travel at a certain speed.
- **Geo-stationary** satellites maintain a fixed position high above the equator by moving at exactly the same rate as the Earth spins. They are used for telecommunications and as weather satellites.
- **Monitoring** satellites (e.g. 'spy satellites') are in a low polar orbit and the Earth spins beneath them, allowing scanning of the whole surface.

GRADE BOOSTER

Remember – all the planets orbit in the same direction and, apart from Pluto, whose orbit is angled at 17°, they form a flat disc.

Question Bank 77

1 Which of these statements explains why objects maintain an orbit?

   a The objects orbiting have a low velocity and are attracted by gravity. ☐

   b The objects orbiting have a high velocity and are repelled by gravity. ☐

   c The objects orbiting have a high velocity and are attracted by gravity. ☐

   d The objects orbiting have a low velocity and are repelled by gravity. ☐

2 True or false?

   The force of gravity between two objects decreases by half if the distance
   between them doubles.

3 True or false?

   When a comet's orbit brings it close to a Sun a vapour trail becomes visible.

4 Which of these statements is **not** true of satellites?

   a Satellites at a fixed distance from the Earth must travel at a
      certain speed. ☐

   b Geo-stationary satellites move at exactly the same rate as
      the Earth spins. ☐

   c Weather satellites are positioned so the Earth spins beneath them. ☐

   d Satellites always travel in the opposite direction to the Earth's spin. ☐

5 Which planet is not orbiting as close to the same plane as the others?

The life of a star

> *The universe has existed for about 15 billion years, but our star (the Sun) is only about 5 billion years old. Where did it come from?*

If material in space is not evenly distributed, then some parts have more gravity than others and will draw material in.

The origin of stars and planets

- Stars form when enough gas and dust in space are attracted together by gravity to promote nuclear fusion.
- Planets form in a similar way, but with less mass.

A star's life cycle

- Formation (as above) and the triggering of nuclear fusion.
- The huge gravitational pull is balanced by expansion caused by high temperatures – so the star remains of fixed size.
- Moderately sized stars (e.g. our Sun) will run short of fuel (hydrogen) and will cool because they lose more heat than is generated.
- The star then cools and expands to become a **red giant**.
- Later, the inner core contracts under gravity to form a hot and dense **white dwarf**.
- This cools to form a **black dwarf**.

Supernovae

Large red supergiants collapse and then explode, throwing dust and gas into space. The remaining core may form an extremely dense **neutron star**. The gas and dust ejected then form new stars and planets – so the cycle begins again.

GRADE BOOSTER
There is no substitute here for learning the sequence by rote – you can't really reason your way to the right order of events.

Question Bank 78

1   What is the missing word?

   When enough material accumulates to form a star,

   nuclear .... starts.

2   Stars remain of fixed size for most of their life because:

   a   Gravitational pull is greater than the expansion caused by the
       heat produced. ☐

   b   Gravitational pull is less than the expansion caused by the
       heat produced. ☐

   c   Gravitational pull does not happen, only expansion caused by
       the heat produced. ☐

   d   Gravitational pull is equal to the expansion caused by the
       heat produced. ☐

3   When stars reach the end of their life, which of these is **not** formed?

   a   white dwarf ☐

   b   neutron star ☐

   c   black dwarf ☐

   d   green giant ☐

4   Complete this paragraph with the missing words:
   planets, core, neutron, collapse.

   Large red supergiants a .... and then explode throwing dust and

   gas into space. The remaining b .... may form an extremely

   dense c .... star. The gas and dust ejected then forms new stars

   and d .... – so the cycle begins again.

5   True or false?

   Supernova is the term for an exploding star.

Looking for life elsewhere

*Life evolved on this planet due to certain conditions – appropriate temperature, liquid water present, the right combination of elements, etc. Given the enormous number of stars (suns) and their planets, is it likely that life has **not** evolved elsewhere?*

How many stars?

To answer this we need to start with our galaxy (the Milky Way).

- We are near the edge in one of its spiral arms. It is flat, so we see most of it as a milky line in the sky.
- There are 200 billion stars in our galaxy.
- Our galaxy is so large that it takes one hundred thousand years for light to cross it.

We are not the only galaxy

- The Milky Way is just one of a thousand billion galaxies in the known universe.

We are not the only planet

- We know that many stars have planets – maybe most do.

If there is life, how would we know?

- Robots can search on other planets (e.g. Mars, or Jupiter's moon Europa) for life or its fossilised remains.
- The monitoring of radio signals in search of intelligent life.
- Analysis of the atmospheres of distant planets to look for atmospheric conditions that could only exist if life is present – e.g. 21 per cent oxygen.

GRADE BOOSTER

To get a sense of scale, our nearest star (excluding the Sun) is Alpha Centauri, 4.3 light-years away. The nearest galaxy is more than 2 million light-years away.

Question Bank 79

1 Our galaxy is called the ....

2 Which of these is in order of size, smallest first?

   a solar system, galaxy, neutron star, universe ☐

   b neutron star, solar system, universe, galaxy ☐

   c neutron star, solar system, galaxy, universe ☐

   d solar system, galaxy, universe, neutron star ☐

3 Which of these is not a likely means of identifying the presence of life on other planets?

   a Robots can search on other planets for fossilised remains. ☐

   b The monitoring of radio signals in search of intelligent life. ☐

   c The use of telescopes on Earth to look for organisms moving. ☐

   d Analysis of the atmospheres of distant planets. ☐

4 True or false?

   Our nearest star is our own Sun.

5 True or false?

   Ten thousand light-years is the time it takes for light to travel 10 000 miles.

Thermal energy transfer

It's fairly obvious that a warm place can rapidly become cold through heat loss – or thermal energy transfer.

Heat energy is transferred by one of three ways: radiation, conduction or convection. Insulation of houses aims to reduce these losses.

Radiation

The amount of radiation given off by an object depends upon:

- how hot it is – a rock at 20°C gives off more infra-red than one at 10°C
- its colour – black objects radiate more than shiny ones.

Note: Radiation is electromagnetic radiation and it can pass through a vacuum.

Conduction

The atoms of hotter objects have more kinetic energy than cooler ones. The vibration of a hotter particle can transfer heat to one with less kinetic energy. Particles are needed for transfer.

Convection

Warmed air or liquid is less dense and rises – heat escapes vertically.

Here are a few examples of building insulation.

Form of insulation	Effective against which loss?
Double glazing (vacuum present)	Conduction, but not radiation
Cavity wall filling	Convection is prevented as air is trapped
Well-sealed doors	Convection losses

GRADE BOOSTER

Make sure you understand heat transfer by radiation, conduction and convection; then you can just work out how different insulation methods work.

Question Bank 80

1 Which means of energy transfer is missing?

   Convection, conduction and ....

2 True or false?

   Humans do not give off white light; we only reflect it.

3 Which of these is not true?

   a Electromagnetic radiation can travel through a vacuum. ☐

   b Convection is the rise of warm air because it is less dense. ☐

   c Conduction cannot happen in a vacuum. ☐

   d Convection is the fall of warm air because it is more dense. ☐

4 Add the missing words to complete the statement:
   more, hotter, transfer, vibration.

   The atoms of a. .... objects have b .... kinetic energy.

   The c .... of hotter particles can transfer heat to one with less

   kinetic energy. Particles are needed for d ....

5 Well-sealed doors significantly reduce the loss of heat by

   ....

Work

Work is one of those words we come across outside of science lessons. From the point of view of physics, somebody sitting at a computer is doing very little work; somebody kicking a ball is doing more work!

■ When a force moves an object, energy is transferred and work is done.
   Work done = energy transferred

Mathematically:

Work done (joules, J) = force applied (newton, N) × distance moved in the direction of the force (m)

Or, more briefly: work = force × distance ($W = F \times D$)

This can be rearranged as: force = work ÷ distance

distance = work ÷ force

Some worked examples

Activity	Amount of work (J)	Force (N)	Distance (m)	Calculation
Pushing a car	?	250	20	$W = F \times D$ $W = 250 \times 20 = 5000J = 5\,kJ$
Crane lifting a weight	?	7000	6	$W = F \times D$ $W = 7000 \times 6 = 42\,000J = 42\,kJ$
Lifting shopping	1200	300	?	$D = W \div F$ $D = 1200 \div 300 = 4\,m$
Weight-lifter	1500	?	1.5	$F = W \div D$ $F = 1500 \div 1.5 = 1000\,N$

Based upon this example do your own calculation at home, using your weight and your stairs:

A person walks up 4 metres of stairs (vertically).
He weighs 700 N (= 70 kg)
Work = 700 × 4 = 2800 J

GRADE BOOSTER

Make up your own examples to practise this. As with most mathematics, repetition fixes the idea in your mind.

Question Bank 81

1 Which of these equations is true?

   a force = distance ÷ work ☐

   b force ÷ work = distance ☐

   c force = distance + work ☐

   d force = work ÷ distance ☐

2 Which combination of units is correct?

   a work (joules), force (newtons) ☐

   b work (watts), force (newtons) ☐

   c work (joules), force (watts) ☐

   d work (kelvins), force (newtons) ☐

3 A 50 kg person walks up 3 m of steps. Calculate the work done.

4 If 1000 J of work is done by lifting a mass by 10 m, calculate the size of the mass.

5 True or false?

   Work is the energy transferred.

Power

Power is another one of those words we come across outside of science lessons. In science, a president ordering military action is using very little power; a parent lifting a baby is using more!

■ Power is a measure of how fast energy is transferred. The greater the power, the more energy is transferred (in a given time).

Mathematically:

power (watt, W) = work done (joule, J) ÷ time taken (seconds, s)
One watt is one joule of energy transferred in one second.
Or, more briefly: energy transferred = power × time

Some worked examples

Activity	Work (J)	Time taken (s)	Calculation of power Work ÷ time
A girl weighing 400 N walks up 3 metres of stairs	$400 \times 3 = 1200$	5	$1200 \div 5 = 240 \,\text{W}$
A girl weighing 400 N walks up 3 metres of stairs	$400 \times 3 = 1200$	2	$1200 \div 2 = 600 \,\text{W}$
Weight-lifter lifts a 500 N weight up 2 metres	$500 \times 2 = 1000$	0.5	$1000 \div 0.5 = 2000 \,\text{W}$

How much energy?

Remember: work = energy transferred

So: power = energy transferred ÷ time
Rearrange to: energy transferred (J) = power (W) × time (s)
You can use this formula to work out how much energy is transferred by various appliances or tools.

100 W light bulb on for 120 seconds (2 mins): energy = $100 \times 120 = 12\,000\,\text{J} = 12\,\text{kJ}$
2 kW kettle boils water in 100 seconds: energy = $2000 \times 100 = 200\,000\,\text{J} = 200\,\text{kJ}$

GRADE BOOSTER

It's important to remember the right units: energy J, work J, power W.

Question Bank 82

1 Insert **one** of these words in this statement:
   much, fast, slowly.

   Power is a measure of how .... energy is transferred. The
   greater the power, the more energy is transferred (in a given time).

2 Which of these is correct?

   a power = work × time ☐

   b power = work ÷ time ☐

   c power = work ÷ time² ☐

   d power = work × energy ☐

3 If 1000 J of work is done in 5 seconds, what is the power?

4 The energy transferred is power × time. If a 2 kW kettle takes 200 seconds to
   boil, how much energy is transferred?

5 Which unit should be written by your answer to question 4?

   a watts ☐

   b newtons ☐

   c joules ☐

   d seconds ☐

Efficiency

> *This is an everyday word, which can mean many things depending upon the context – 'have you worked efficiently today?' In physics, efficiency refers to the extent to which the energy is usefully transferred – i.e. not wasted.*

An everyday example of this is a motor car. Chemical energy (e.g. petrol) is combusted (burned) to provide energy of motion (kinetic energy); but most is wasted as:

- sound – the engine noise and the noise of tyres on roads and air on the body
- heat – the engine has to be cooled by water
- incomplete combustion – particles in the exhaust (soot) are a waste.

Here is a diagram showing efficiency of a coal-powered power station:

- The energy wasted is transferred to the environment, which becomes warmer.
- As it spreads further, it becomes more difficult to make use of it.

Mathematically:

efficiency = useful energy transferred by a device ÷ total energy supplied to the device × 100%

Here are a few examples.

Device	Energy in (J/second)	Energy out (J/second)	Efficiency (÷ 100 for %)
Light bulb	100	Heat 80, light 20	20 ÷ 100 = 0.2 or 20%
Low-energy light bulb	25	Heat 5, light 20	20 ÷ 25 = 0.8 or 80%
Television	200	Heat 150, light + sound 50	50 ÷ 200 = 0.25 or 25%

GRADE BOOSTER

Stick to precise definitions in science – don't let yourself drift into using terms in an everyday sense.

Question Bank 83

1 When a car runs, energy is wasted. Which of these would account for the biggest losses?

  a heat energy and sound energy ☐

  b kinetic energy and sound energy ☐

  c sound energy and elastic potential energy ☐

  d heat energy and gravitational potential energy ☐

2 If fuels burn inefficiently and particles of soot are found in the exhaust, this is:

  a a sign of a well-tuned engine ☐

  b a sign that little energy has been wasted ☐

  c a sign of incomplete combustion and energy wastage ☐

  d a sign of sound energy being transferred to the environment ☐

3 Yes or no?

  If heat energy from a power station spreads further, does it become more difficult to use it?

4 A light bulb uses 200J/s of energy and gives out 140J/s of light. What is its efficiency?

5 If a television uses 400J/s of energy and gives out 160J/s of heat, what is its efficiency?

Forms of energy

Energy is yet another one of those words we come across outside of science lessons. A boy lying and doing nothing on a top bunk has more (potential) energy than one reading Shakespeare on the bottom bunk.

Any object capable of doing work is said to have energy.

Energy can be transferred and stored in several forms:

- heat
- light
- kinetic
- sound
- elastic (potential)
- chemical (potential)
- gravitational (potential).

There is an important distinction here between potential energy and the others.

- **Potential energy** is stored energy, which can be transferred. For example, a match only releases its potential energy when struck; the energy is then transferred as light and heat.

- **Gravitational potential energy** is the energy stored in an object due to its height – it has been lifted there against the force of gravity.

The Earth has a gravitational field strength of about 10 N/kg.

An object's **weight** is due to the gravitational force that acts on the mass:

weight (N) = mass (kg) × gravitational field strength (N/kg)

So a person of mass 50 kg has a weight of $50 \times 10 = 500$ N.

If this person is standing 2 metres up a ladder, their gravitational potential energy (J) is:

Gravitational potential energy (J) =
mass (kg) × gravitational field strength (N/kg) × height (m)

$$PE = 50 \times 10 \times 2 = 1000 \, J = 1 \, kJ$$

GRADE BOOSTER

These formulae are too wordy to recall. Remember to multiply a *mass* by 10 to get the *weight* (40 kg × 10 = 400 N). Then PE = weight (N) × height (m).

Question Bank 84

1 Which of these lists are **only** examples of potential energy?

   a sound, gravitational, heat ☐

   b elastic, gravitational, chemical ☐

   c chemical, gravitational, sound ☐

   d kinetic, chemical, light ☐

2 True or false?

   Potential energy is stored energy.

3 With a gravitational field strength of 10N/kg, what is the weight of a 100kg mass?

4 Which unit should you record beside your answer to question 3?

   a joules ☐

   b newtons ☐

   c watts ☐

   d seconds ☐

5 If a person with a weight of 500N is 6m up a ladder, what is their gravitational potential energy?

Energy calculations

*On the previous page you read about gravitational potential energy. If the person on the ladder now jumps off, the potential energy becomes **kinetic**.*

■ Kinetic energy is the energy an object has because of its movement.

Let's start with some gravitational **potential** energy.

A crane lifts a mass of 1000 kg to a height of 50 metres.

Change in gravitational potential energy (PE) = 1000 × 10 × 50 = 500 000 J

If the mass is now lowered at a fixed speed of 10 metres per second (m/s), then it will have a **kinetic** energy of:

kinetic energy (J) = $\frac{1}{2}$ × mass (kg) × speed^2 (m/s)^2

Or KE = $\frac{1}{2}mv^2$

KE = 0.5 × 1000 × 10^2 = 50 000 J = 50 kJ

Here are some more examples of kinetic energy calculations.

Example	Speed (m/s)	Mass (kg)	Kinetic energy (J) = $\frac{1}{2}mv^2$
A car moving	20	1000	0.5 × 1000 × 20^2 = 200 000 J = 200 kJ
A lorry moving	10	4000	0.5 × 4000 × 10^2 = 200 000 J = 200 kJ

The slower lorry has the same kinetic energy because its mass is larger.

■ One other form of potential energy is **elastic potential energy**. This is defined as the energy stored in an elastic substance when work is done to distort it.

The child does work (puffs) to blow it up.
The elastic walls gain elastic potential energy.

GRADE BOOSTER

Energy cannot be lost, only transferred. When the balloon pops, elastic energy is transferred as sound.

Question Bank 85

1 Kinetic energy is the energy an object has due to its:

   a position ☐

   b chemical constituents ☐

   c movement ☐

   d gravitational potential energy ☐

2 Calculate the kinetic energy of an object of mass 100 kg travelling at 5 m/s.

3 Which of these has the greater kinetic energy?

   a a rock of mass 1 kg travelling at 6 m/s ☐

   b a rock of mass 2 kg travelling at 3 m/s ☐

   c a rock of mass 3 kg travelling at 2 m/s ☐

   d a rock of mass 4 kg travelling at 1 m/s ☐

4 True or false?

   To stretch an elastic band, work has to be done. The more work done, the more elastic potential energy there is.

5 True or false?

   Energy is lost when it is transferred.

The motor effect

We rely upon the motor effect every day – it starts your car (starter motor) and it dries your hair (hairdryer).

The motor effect is the force that acts on an electric current as it passes through a magnetic field.

- The force direction is at right angles to the direction of both the current and the magnetic field.
- If the magnetic field or the current is reversed, so is the direction of the force.

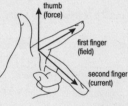

To make this easier to work out, we use
Fleming's left-hand rule.

ThuMb = Movement
First finger = Field
SeCond finger = Current

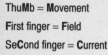

Note the following key points:

- The force can be increased by using stronger magnets and/or a larger current.
- The commutator (split ring) reverses the current in the wire each time it reaches the vertical – this is essential to keep the coil turning in the same direction.

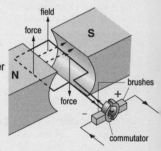

GRADE BOOSTER

Practise Fleming's left-hand rule.

Question Bank 86

1 Add one word to complete the statement; choose from:
pressure, **energy**, **force**.

The motor effect is the .... that acts on an electric current as it passes through a magnetic field.

2 In a motor the force direction is.

   a at right angles to the current but not the magnetic field ☐

   b at right angles to the magnetic field but not the current ☐

   c at right angles to the current and the magnetic field ☐

   d at right angles to neither the current or the magnetic field ☐

3 In Fleming's left-hand rule, which of these is true?

   a The thuMb is for movement and the First finger is for force. ☐

   b The thuMb is for magnetic field and the First finger is for force. ☐

   c The thuMb is for magnetic field and the First finger is for field. ☐

   d The thuMb is for movement and the First finger is for field. ☐

4 Choose the missing word.

In a simple d.c. motor the force can be increased by using stronger magnets and a .... current.

   a larger

   b smaller

5 True or false?

To keep a coil turning, the split ring is used to reverse the current.

Electromagnetic induction

> *It helps here to understand the term induction. If something is **induced**, it is made to happen.*

If a wire (or coil) cuts through a magnetic field, a voltage is induced – this causes a current.

Or more simply:

- Electricity can be generated by rotating a coil of wire in a magnetic field.
- Electricity can be generated by rotating a magnet inside a coil of wire.

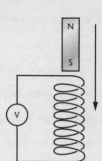

The size of the induced voltage increases if:

- the area of the coil is larger
- the number of turns in the coil is increased
- the magnetic field strength is increased
- the speed of movement increases.

How is this put to use?

- In electrical generators, an electromagnet rotates in a copper coil. To generate a voltage with a frequency of 50 Hz, the electromagnet rotates at 3000 revolutions per minute.

GRADE BOOSTER

Most means of generating electricity require sources of energy to cause rotation of turbines; these in turn rotate the electromagnet in a generator. Think of wind turbines.

Question Bank 87

1   Choose one of these words to complete the sentence:
    introduced, influenced, induced, indirect.

    If a coil cuts through a magnetic field, a voltage is ...., which
    causes a current.

2   True or false?

    Electricity can be generated by rotating a magnet in a coil of wire.

3   Which of these will **not** increase the voltage?

    a   The area of the coil is larger.

    b   The number of turns in the coil is increased.

    c   The magnetic field strength is decreased.

    d   The speed of movement increases.

4   True or false?

    In an electrical generator, a coil rotates in an electromagnet.

5   Choose **two** of these words to complete the sentence:
    pushing, rotation, generator.

    Most means of generating electricity require sources of energy to cause

    a .... of turbines; these in turn rotate the electromagnet in a

    b ....

Transformers

You probably know that electricity is supplied to you at 230 V, but when you see overhead pylon wires, remember the voltage is 400 000 V.

When current flows, energy is lost as heat. With high voltages and low currents, energy losses are reduced.

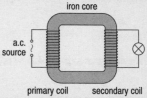

- **Transformers** step up and step down the voltages to minimise energy losses and to provide electricity to homes at a safer voltage. Note that transformers only work with a.c.

- The current in the primary coil sets up a changing magnetic field in the iron core.

- The changing magnetic field induces a voltage in the secondary coil.

- To step up (increase) the voltage there are more turns in the secondary coil.

- To step down there are more coils in the primary coil.

Note: As $V = IR$, an increase in voltage reduces the current and vice versa.

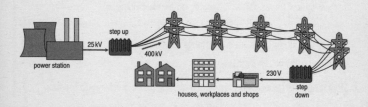

GRADE BOOSTER

To calculate step-ups and step-downs, remember the ratio of the number of coils is the same as the ratio for the voltages.

Question Bank 88

1 Choose from these words to complete the sentences:

sound, light, high, heat, low.

When current flows energy is lost as **a** .... With high

voltages and **b** .... currents, energy losses are reduced.

2 True or false?

Transformers change the voltage to make transfer of energy more efficient.

3 Which of these alternatives will step up (increase) the voltage?

a More coils in the primary than secondary coil ☐

b More coils in the secondary than primary coil ☐

4 As $V = IR$ this shows that with an increase in voltage, the current is:

a the same ☐

b increased ☐

c decreased ☐

d modulated ☐

5 True or false?

The voltage in overhead pylon wires is much higher than the voltage
in a house.

Energy resources and uses

> With increasing human populations and increasing demand for modern
> conveniences, our world energy consumption is guaranteed to rise for many
> decades to come. How will we meet the increasing demand?

Renewable energy sources will not run out, non-renewable will.

Non-renewable energy sources include:

- fossil fuels (coal, gas and oil)
- nuclear fuel.

Strictly speaking, fossil fuels are renewing, but at a vastly slower rate than we use them.

Renewable sources include:

- sunlight
- wind
- waves
- running water
- tides
- geothermal
- trees.

Strictly speaking, trees are only renewable if we grow them at the same rate as we use them.

The generation of electricity

Electricity is a very convenient energy source. It is usually generated by the spinning of turbines in power generators, which produce the electricity. The key issue is the origin of the energy to do this.

- Heat from the burning of fossil fuels heats water to form steam that drives the turbines.
- Controlled nuclear reactions (uranium or plutonium fuel) produce heat to make steam.
- Wind, waves or water running downhill (hydroelectric) can directly spin turbines.
- Steam rising from geothermal vents can also be used (nuclear reactions in the Earth produce the heat).

The use of solar (photovoltaic) cells is different because electricity is produced directly. Solar energy can also heat water for domestic use.

GRADE BOOSTER

You can pick up a lot of information on this from sources other than science lessons. Be careful, though, that you stick to proper scientific definitions.

Question Bank 89

1 True or false?

World energy consumption is increasing with population and people's demand for modern conveniences.

2 Which of these lists is **not** all renewable sources?

  a Wind, waves and solar ☐

  b Wind, tides and solar ☐

  c Wind, waves and geothermal ☐

  d Wind, waves and nuclear ☐

3 True or false?

Trees are renewable if we use them a little bit faster than they are replaced.

4 Choose two of these words to complete the sentence:

transformers,   turbines,   generators,   magnets.

Most electricity is generated by heat sources creating steam to turn

a ...., to power **b** ....

5 True or false?

Solar energy can be used to produce electricity directly and to heat water.

Renewable vs. non-renewable energy

It's easy to be captivated by the arguments for using renewable energy sources, but to argue the case you need to appreciate that there are arguments against as well as for.

We have to get our energy from somewhere. If a potential source is very inefficient, it is not cost-effective to use.

Energy source	Advantages	Disadvantages
Fossil fuels	Countries have spent money investing in power stations to use this fuel Gas and oil are relatively easy to transport (in pipes) There is currently a lot of easily available fuel	Carbon dioxide pollution adding a greenhouse gas to the atmosphere – causing global warming Sulphur dioxide pollution, forming sulphuric acid and causing acid rain
Nuclear fuels	There is currently a lot of nuclear fuel available No gases generated – i.e. CO_2 In principle they can be built anywhere, as not much nuclear fuel needs to be moved	Accidents – there must be no leakage of radioactive material Nuclear power stations are expensive to build Nuclear waste lasts a long time and is expensive to dispose of
Wind turbines	'Free energy' Non-polluting	Need wind! Only certain sites are usable (hills, coastline), and wind does not always blow The best sites have amenity value (for tourists) Wind turbines are noisy and unsightly
Tidal power	'Free energy' Non-polluting Unlike wind, tides are regular	If barrages are built they damage the coastal ecosystems

GRADE BOOSTER

Never get carried away by your own feelings about renewable resources – they are not all good. Learn the facts.

Question Bank 90

1 True or false?

   Renewable energy sources are replaced as least as fast as they are used.

2 Which combination of energy sources is renewable?

   a fossil fuel and nuclear

   b fossil fuels and wind

   c wind and tidal

   d nuclear and wind

3 Which of these is **not** true of wind power?

   a It is renewable.

   b It is non-renewable.

   c It is a potential eyesore.

   d It can be noisy.

4 True or false?

   Using the power of the tides may damage coastal ecosystems.

5 True or false?

   Burning fossil fuels produces carbon dioxide that damages the ozone layer.

Radioactivity 1

> *The word 'radiation' is often not used precisely. Make sure you understand the difference between radiation like radio waves and radiation from radioactive materials.*

For this topic, 'radiation' means high-energy ionising radiation.

- Ionising radiation collides with neutral atoms and ionises them – it knocks off electrons, leaving positively charged ions.
- The larger the radiation dose, the more damage is caused to the DNA of living cells, causing death or cancer.
- Ionising radiation does more damage to dividing cells (cancer cells divide often), so controlled doses of radiation can kill cancer cells.

Radioactive materials give off radiation all the time. There are three types of radiation, as shown in this table.

Type of radiation	Penetrating power	Threat to living cells
alpha, α (helium nuclei – two protons and two neutrons)	Stopped by a few centimetres of air, or thin paper	Outside the body – unlikely to reach cells. Inside – most dangerous as it is readily absorbed
beta, β (high-energy electrons)	Stopped by a few centimetres of metal	Outside – can easily reach cells. Inside – less dangerous than alpha, as most 'misses' DNA
gamma, γ (short-wavelength electromagnetic radiation)	Only stopped by many centimetres of lead or metres of concrete	Less dangerous than beta

Background radiation

We are exposed to ionising radiation all the time as it is given off by local rocks and from the Sun. However, some places have much more than others – in Britain, granite rocks (e.g. in Devon/Cornwall) emit radon gas that is breathed in and produces alpha particles, which can cause lung cancer.

GRADE BOOSTER

A radiation badge 'fogs' with exposure to ionising radiation. The quicker it fogs, the higher the dose received.

Question Bank 91

1 True or false?

Radio waves are a form of ionising radiation.

2 True or false?

Ionising radiation causes more damage to cancer cells than normal cells.

3 Which type of radiation can be stopped by a thin sheet of paper?

   a alpha ☐

   b beta ☐

   c X-rays ☐

   d gamma ☐

4 Which of these is true?

   a Alpha radiation consists of helium nuclei. ☐

   b Beta radiation is stopped by thin paper. ☐

   c Gamma is the least penetrative. ☐

   d Alpha is only stopped by a few centimetres of lead. ☐

5 Choose from these words to complete the statement:
radon, **evenly**, **rock**, **alpha**.

Background radiation is caused by radiation from some types of **a** ....;
it is not found **b** .... throughout the country. The presence of
c .... gas is particularly dangerous as it emits **d** ....
particles, which cause lung cancer.

Radioactivity 2

> *You've studied atomic structure in chemistry and should already know about protons, neutrons and electrons.*

Radioactivity occurs due to changes in the nuclei of atoms (nuclear changes). The β-particles (electrons) therefore come from the nucleus, not the electron shells.

Some history

The firing of alpha particles at gold leaf (a few atoms thick) resulted in a few bouncing back. This told Rutherford and Marsden (the researchers) that atoms are mainly space with a very small, dense nucleus, around which electrons orbit.

Radioisotopes

Isotopes are atoms of elements with differing numbers of neutrons. Some isotopes have unstable nuclei that disintegrate – they are radioactive isotopes or radioisotopes.

Unstable nuclei give off radioactive particles (e.g. α, β, or γ) and cause the proton number to change.

Remember – the proton number is the atomic number and determines which element is present. Change the proton number and the element changes. This explains why uranium decays to lead.

Half-life

In this time half the atoms of the original radioactive substance decay, and the count rate also falls to half. Rocks can be dated using known half-lives. Uranium-238 (half-life 4.5 billion years) decays to lead-206. The relative amount of the two indicates when magma was produced.

GRADE BOOSTER

Don't learn the same facts twice (see protons, electrons and neutrons in chemistry topics). Try to spot links between topics and between subjects.

Question Bank 92

1 True or false?

   Beta radiation comes from the electron shells of atoms.

2 If alpha particles do **not** rebound off a very thin sheet of gold, this shows:

   a that gold atoms are very dense ☐

   b that gold does not corrode ☐

   c that gold atoms are mainly space ☐

   d that the nucleus is very dense ☐

3 Isotopes of elements have different numbers of:

   a electrons ☐

   b neutrons ☐

   c protons ☐

   d shells ☐

4 True or false?

   The proton number determines which element is which.

5 If a radioactive material decays for **two** half-lives, its radioactive count rate will be:

   a half the original ☐

   b double the original ☐

   c treble the original ☐

   d quarter the original ☐

Periodic Table

KEY:
Atomic mass
Symbol
Name
Atomic Number

Transition elements

1	2	3	4	5	6	7	8	9	10	11	12	3	4	5	6	7	0
1 **H** Hydrogen 1																	4 **He** Helium 2
7 **Li** Lithium 3	9 **Be** Beryllium 4											11 **B** Boron 5	12 **C** Carbon 6	14 **N** Nitrogen 7	16 **O** Oxygen 8	19 **F** Fluorine 9	20 **Ne** Neon 10
23 **Na** Sodium 11	24 **Mg** Magnesium 12											27 **Al** Aluminium 13	28 **Si** Silicon 14	31 **P** Phosphorus 15	32 **S** Sulphur 16	35.5 **Cl** Chlorine 17	40 **Ar** Argon 18
39 **K** Potassium 19	40 **Ca** Calcium 20	45 **Sc** Scandium 21	48 **Ti** Titanium 22	51 **V** Vanadium 23	52 **Cr** Chromium 24	55 **Mn** Manganese 25	56 **Fe** Iron 26	59 **Co** Cobalt 27	59 **Ni** Nickel 28	64 **Cu** Copper 29	65 **Zn** Zinc 30	70 **Ga** Gallium 31	73 **Ge** Germanium 32	75 **As** Arsenic 33	79 **Se** Selenium 34	80 **Br** Bromine 35	84 **Kr** Krypton 36
85.5 **Rb** Rubidium 37	88 **Sr** Strontium 38	89 **Y** Yttrium 39	91 **Zr** Zirconium 40	93 **Nb** Niobium 41	96 **Mo** Molybdenum 42	**Tc** Technetium 43	101 **Ru** Ruthenium 44	103 **Rh** Rhodium 45	106 **Pd** Palladium 46	108 **Ag** Silver 47	112 **Cd** Cadmium 48	115 **In** Indium 49	119 **Sn** Tin 50	122 **Sb** Antimony 51	128 **Te** Tellurium 52	127 **I** Iodine 53	131 **Xe** Xenon 54
133 **Cs** Caesium 55	137 **Ba** Barium 56	139 **La** Lanthanum 57	178.5 **Hf** Hafnium 72	181 **Ta** Tantalum 73	184 **W** Tungsten 74	186 **Re** Rhenium 75	190 **Os** Osmium 76	192 **Ir** Iridium 77	195 **Pt** Platinum 78	197 **Au** Gold 79	210 **Hg** Mercury 80	204 **Tl** Thallium 81	207 **Pb** Lead 82	209 **Bi** Bismuth 83	210 **Po** Polonium 84	210 **At** Astatine 85	222 **Rn** Radon 86
223 **Fr** Francium 87	226 **Ra** Radium 88	227 **Ac** Actinium 89	**Db** Dubnium 104	**Jl** Joliotium 105	**Rf** Rutherfordium 106	**Bh** Bohrium 107	**Hn** Hahnium 108	**Mt** Meitnerium 109									

Lanthanides

139 **La** Lanthanum 57	140 **Ce** Cerium 58	141 **Pr** Praseodymium 59	144 **Nd** Neodymium 60	147 **Pm** Promethium 61	150 **Sm** Samarium 62	152 **Eu** Europium 63	157 **Gd** Gadolinium 64	159 **Tb** Terbium 65	162.5 **Dy** Dysprosium 66	165 **Ho** Holmium 67	167 **Er** Erbium 68	169 **Tm** Thulium 69	175 **Yb** Ytterbium 70	175 **Lu** Lutetium 71

Actinides

227 **Ac** Actinium 89	232 **Th** Thorium 90	231 **Pa** Protactinium 91	238 **U** Uranium 92	237 **Np** Neptunium 93	242 **Pu** Plutonium 94	243 **Am** Americium 95	247 **Cm** Curium 96	247 **Bk** Berkelium 97	251 **Cf** Californium 98	254 **Es** Einsteinium 99	253 **Fm** Fermium 100	256 **Md** Mendelevium 101	254 **No** Nobelium 102	257 **Lw** Lawrencium 103

Question Bank Answers

Biology

Question Bank 1
1 **a** digest
  b absorb
  c faeces
2 c
3 c
4 True
5 True

Question Bank 2
1 c
2 **a** catalysts
  b specific
  c active site
  d substrate
3 d
4 False
5 d

Question Bank 3
1 **a** = (iii)
  b = (i)
  c = (ii)
2 a
3 Surface area
4 b
5 False

Question Bank 4
1 **a** = (iii)
  b = (iv)
  c = (i)
  d = (ii)
2 b
3 Carbon dioxide
4 Oxygen
5 Insulin

Question Bank 5
1 a
2 b
3 c
4 Artery
5 Vein

Question Bank 6
1 Oxygen
2 Carbon dioxide
3 d
4 a
5 Alveoli

Question Bank 7
1 False
2 d
3 a
4 True
5 False

Question Bank 8
1 Kidney
2 c
3 b
4 c
5 False

Question Bank 9
1 c
2 True
3 c
4 b
5 True

Question Bank 10
1 Touch
2 d
3 False
4 d
5 b

Question Bank 11
1 c
2 a
3 a = receptors
  b = impulses
  c = CNS
  d = effectors
4 True
5 False

Question Bank 12
1 True
2 b
3 a
4 b
5 Yes

Question Bank 13
1 d
2 True
3 b
4 True
5 a

Question Bank 14
1 False
2 a = palisade
  b = chloroplasts
  c = rectangular
  d = cell walls
3 True
4 Glucose
5 c

Question Bank 15
1 True
2 a
3 a = root hairs,
  b = water
  c = xylem
  d = turgid
4 a
5 Phloem

Question Bank 16
1 a = gametes
  b = fertilisation
  c = female
  d = clones
2 True
3 c
4 Pituitary
5 True

Question Bank 17
1 a
2 True
3 c
4 Environment
5 d

Question Bank 18
1 c
2 b
3 d
4 True
5 c

Question Bank 19
1 a = mutant
  b = rare
  c = disease
  d = carrier
2 b
3 c
4 c
5 a

Question Bank 20
1 No
2 a = nucleus
  b = DNA
  c = mixed
  d = protein
3 a
4 True
5 False

Question Bank 21

1 c
2 d
3 True
4 True
5 **a** = offspring
  b = competition
  c = vary
  d = adapted
  e = genes

Question Bank 22

1 True
2 b
3 True
4 **a** = extinction
  b = fossils
  c = ancestors
  d = evolutionary
5 a

Question Bank 23

1 b
2 **a** yielding
  b mother
  c semen
  d generation
3 c
4 True
5 a

Question Bank 24

1 a
2 True
3 d
4 d
5 False

Question Bank 25

1 c
2 **a** = up
  b = multiply
  c = eaten
  d = rise
3 c
4 a
5 True

Question Bank 26

1 True
2 c
3 No
4 Yes
5 d

Question Bank 27

1 b
2 b
3 c
4 Rabbit
5 False

Question Bank 28

1 True
2 d
3 c
4 True
5 Carbon dioxide

Question Bank 29

1 c
2 f
3 a
4 b
5 d
6 e

Question Bank 30

1 e
2 d
3 f
4 b
5 c
6 a

Question Bank 31

1 c
2 e
3 a
4 b
5 f
6 d

Question Bank 32
1 f
2 c
3 a
4 e
5 d
6 b

Question Bank 33
1 b
2 False
3 a
4 c
5 3

Question Bank 34
1 Potassium
2 **a** = positive
  b = negative
  c = neutral
3 12
4 a
5 d

Question Bank 35
1 14
2 20
3 c
4 True
5 None

Question Bank 36
1 True
2 c
3 c
4 c
5 False

Question Bank 37
1 a
2 Neutrons
3 True
4 **a** = neutrons
  b = electron
  c = negative
5 False

Question Bank 38
1 Metallic
2 b
3 a
4 d
5 True

Question Bank 39
1 Metallic
2 Covalent
3 Ionic
4 b
5 c

Question Bank 40
1 c
2 Carbon dioxide
3 c
4 **a** = non-biodegradable
  b = accumulate
  c = enzymes
5 Sulphur dioxide

Question Bank 41
1 d
2 True
3 4
4 d
5 C_3H_8

Question Bank 42
1 c
2 True
3 Crinoids
4 c
5 Calcium carbonate

Question Bank 43
1 **a** = temperature
  b = texture
  c = melting
  d = recrystallisation
2 Crystals
3 d
4 True
5 Above ground or outside the Earth's crust

Question Bank 44
1 c
2 Thermal decomposition
3 Small stones
4 Limestone
5 c

Question Bank 45
1 True
2 a
3 c
4 True
5 a

Question Bank 46
1 Bauxite
2 c
3 True
4 d
5 Cathode

Question Bank 47
1 b
2 Iron
3 a
4 a
5 False

Question Bank 48
1 b
2 a
3 d
4 False
5 a

Question Bank 49
1 74
2 40
3 32
4 71
5 34

Question Bank 50
1 c
2 b
3 UV
4 Burning of fossil fuels
5 True

Question Bank 51
1 a
2 d
3 b
4 c
5 False

Question Bank 52
1 2, 3
2 2, 5
3 2, 8
4 2, 8, 3
5 2, 8, 7

Question Bank 53
1 c
2 b
3 Copper
4 Iron
5 Copper

Question Bank 54
1 1
2 potassium
3 a = red
  b = lilac
  c = orange
4 Yes
5 d

Question Bank 55
1 True
2 b
3 7
4 Chlorine
5 a

Question Bank 56
1 True
2 False
3 c
4 Neon
5 False

Question Bank 57
1 d
2 Carbon dioxide
3 Oxygen
4 c
5 a

Question Bank 58
1 Hydrogen
2 c
3 d
4 c
5 False

Question Bank 59
1 **a** = temperature
  b = kinetic
  c = collisions
2 a
3 True
4 True
5 d

Question Bank 60
1 Protein
2 d
3 True
4 **a** = catalysts
  b = enzymes
  c = denatured
5 c

Question Bank 61
1 True
2 d
3 Carbon dioxide
4 c
5 Calcium carbonate

Question Bank 62
1 d
2 a
3 False
4 c
5 True

Physics

Question Bank 63
1 b
2 a
3 True
4 c
5 b

Question Bank 64
1 d
2 a
3 False
4 True
5 increases

Question Bank 65
1 d
2 False
3 True
4 0.7p
5 1 kW

Question Bank 66
1 **a** = (iii)
  b = (i)
  c = (ii)
2 a
3 **a** = metal
  b = earthed
  c = ground
  d = resistance
4 False
5 b

Question Bank 67
1 a
2 b
3 **a** = charged
  b = opposite
  c = reversing
  d = image
4 Earthed
5 Charge

Question Bank 68
1 b
2 c
3 False
4 True
5 False

Question Bank 69
1 a
2 **a** = size
  b = unbalanced
  c = increase
  d = slows
3 False
4 True
5 Forwards

Question Bank 70
1 6m
2 3m
3 9m
4 c
5 True

Question Bank 71
1 A
2 B
3 b
4 a
5 False

Question Bank 72
1 30°
2 b
3 False
4 d
5 False

Question Bank 73
1 False
2 a
3 b
4 42
5 False

Question Bank 74
1 True
2 c
3 False
4 a
5 c

Question Bank 75
1 d
2 c
3 b
4 a
5 False

Question Bank 76
1 True
2 d
3 b
4 True
5 c

Question Bank 77
1 c
2 False
3 True
4 d
5 Pluto

Question Bank 78
1 Reactions or fusion
2 d
3 d
4 **a** = collapse
  b = core
  c = neutron
  d = planets
5 True

Question Bank 79
1 Milky Way
2 c
3 c
4 True
5 False

Question Bank 80
1 Radiation
2 True
3 d
4 **a** = hotter
  b = more
  c = vibration
  d = transfer
5 Convection

Question Bank 81
1 d
2 a
3 1500 J
4 10 kg
5 True

Question Bank 82
1 Fast
2 b
3 200 J/s or 200 W
4 400 kJ
5 c

Question Bank 83
1 a
2 c
3 Yes
4 70%
5 60%

Question Bank 84
1 b
2 True
3 1000 N
4 b
5 3000 J

Question Bank 85
1 c
2 1250 J
3 a
4 True
5 False

Question Bank 86
1 Force
2 c
3 d

4 a
5 True

Question Bank 87
1 Induced
2 True
3 c
4 False
5 **a** = rotation
  b = generator

Question Bank 88
1 **a** = heat
  b = low
2 True
3 b
4 c
5 True

Question Bank 89
1 True
2 d
3 False
4 **a** = turbines
  b = generators
5 True

Question Bank 90
1 True
2 c
3 b
4 True
5 False

Question Bank 91
1 False
2 True
3 a
4 a
5 **a** = rock
  b = evenly
  c = radon
  d = alpha

Question Bank 92
1 False
2 c
3 b
4 True
5 d

Scoring Grid

Question bank no.	topic	score
1	Digestion	/5
2	Enzymes	/5
3	Digestive enzymes	/5
4	Functions of blood	/5
5	Circulation and vessels	/5
6	Gas exchange	/5
7	Breathing and respiration	/5
8	Homeostasis 1	/5
9	Homeostasis 2	/5
10	Nervous system	/5
11	Reflexes	/5
12	Disease and drugs	/5
13	Diffusion and osmosis	/5
14	Leaves and photosynthesis	/5
15	Transpiration and transport in plants	/5
16	Reproduction	/5
17	Cell division, mutation and variation	/5
18	Genetics 1	/5
19	Genetics 2	/5
20	Genetic engineering	/5
21	Natural selection	/5
22	Evolution – the evidence	/5
23	Artificial selection and cloning	/5
24	Adaptation	/5
25	Communities	/5
26	Pyramids of biomass and number	/5
27	Energy transfer in habitats	/5
28	Carbon cycle	/5
29	People and the environment	/6
30	Cell structure	/6
31	Cell specialisation	/6
32	Safety symbols	/6
33	Elements, compounds and mixtures	/5
34	Atomic structure	/5
35	Atomic mass and number	/5
36	Electron shells and reactivity	/5
37	Isotopes and ions	/5
38	Bonding 1	/5
39	Bonding 2	/5
40	Cracking, hydrocarbon combustion and plastics	/5
41	Crude oil	/5
42	The rock record 1	/5
43	The rock record 2	/5
44	Rocks and their products	/5
45	Extracting metals from ores	/5
46	Metals from ores – electrolysis	/5
47	Nitrogen and fertilisers	/5
48	Chemical equations	/5
49	Relative atomic mass	/5
50	The atmosphere and oceans	/5
51	Periodic table 1	/5
52	Periodic table 2	/5
53	The transition elements	/5
54	The alkali metals	/5
55	The halogens	/5
56	The noble gases	/5
57	Rates of reaction 1	/5
58	Rates of reaction 2	/5
59	Rates of reaction 3	/5
60	Enzymes 1	/5
61	Enzymes 2	/5
62	Types of chemical reaction	/5
63	Series and parallel circuits	/5
64	Current and resistance	/5
65	Electrical appliances and costs	/5
66	Mains electricity and safety	/5
67	Electrical charge	/5
68	Distance–time and velocity–time graphs	/5
69	Forces, acceleration and friction	/5
70	Braking distances and falling objects	/5
71	Waves 1	/5
72	Waves 2	/5
73	Light as a wave	/5
74	Electromagnetic spectrum 1	/5
75	Electromagnetic spectrum 2	/5
76	The Earth's structure	/5
77	The solar system	/5
78	The life of a star	/5
79	Looking for life elsewhere	/5
80	Thermal energy transfer	/5
81	Work	/5
82	Power	/5
83	Efficiency	/5
84	Forms of energy	/5
85	Energy calculations	/5
86	The motor effect	/5
87	Electromagnetic induction	/5
88	Transformers	/5
89	Energy resources and uses	/5
90	Renewable vs. non-renewable energy	/5
91	Radioactivity 1	/5
92	Radioactivity 2	/5

Glossary

Acceleration	a change in velocity, negative = deceleration
Activation energy	the energy required to start a reaction
Active site	the part of the surface of an enzyme where a substrate binds
Adaptation	the evolution of a specialisation that improves the chance of survival
Alkali metal	metals in group 1 of the periodic table e.g. sodium
Alleles	different forms of a gene – e.g. allele for blue eyes
Alloy	different metal elements combined – e.g. copper and zinc = brass
Alpha particle	a helium nucleus emitted by a radioactive material
Alternating current	a current that changes direction
Alveoli	gas exchange surface in the lung – formed from flattened cells
Amplitude of a wave	the maximum displacement from the mean position
Antibody	a precisely shaped protein that binds to a foreign molecule (antigen)
Antigen	a foreign molecule that induces an immune response
Arteries	blood vessels that take blood away from the heart
Beta radiation	electrons emitted from the nucleus of radioactive elements
Bile salts	disperse fat to increase surface area for action of lipase
Capillaries	tiny blood vessels with walls one cell thick – exchange happens
Community	all the organisms of all species in a habitat
Compound	molecules formed from atoms of different elements
Cracking	thermal decomposition of hydrocarbons of crude oil
Current	flow of electric charge
Diffraction	spreading out of a wave as it passes an object or goes through a gap
Diffusion	particles randomly moving spread out
Diode	only allows current to pass in one direction
Direct current	the current flows in only one direction
Electrolysis	use of electricity to split particles – e.g. aluminium from oxygen
Electron	a negatively charged and very light particle
Element	pure substance made up of atoms of one kind

Enzymes	protein catalysts
Eutrophication	the nutrient enrichment of water promoting algal blooms
Frequency of waves	the number of waves that pass a point in a second
Gametes	sex cells, sperm and egg
Gamma radiation	very short wavelength electromagnetic radiation
Halogen	elements of group 7 of the periodic table, e.g. chlorine
Homeostasis	maintaining constant internal conditions, e.g. temperature
Hormone	a chemical messenger, molecule, e.g. insulin
Hydrocarbon	a compound made of hydrogen and carbon, e.g. ethene, C_2H_4
Ion	a charged particle, e.g. K^+, SO_4^{2-}
Isotope	atoms of an element with differing numbers of neutrons
Kilowatt hour	a kW of energy transferred each second for one hour
Mass number	the number of protons and neutrons in an atoms of an element
Molecule	atoms bonded together
Negative feedback	the correction of a condition back to normal, e.g. body temperature
Neutron	uncharged particles in the nucleus of an atom
Noble gas	elements of group 7 of the periodic, have full outer shells
Metal ore	a metal combined with another element
Osmosis	the net diffusion of water through a semi-permeable membrane
Power	how fast energy is transferred
Proton	a positively charged particle in the nucleus of an atom
Receptors	specialised cells that are sensitive to one kind of stimulus
Refraction	the change in speed when waves pass from one material to another
Renewable	an energy source that is replaced as fast as it is used
Substrate	a molecule that combines with the active site of an enzyme
Tectonics	the slow motion of the plates that form the Earth's crust
Transformer	a devise that can step up or step down an alternating current
Transpiration	the evaporation of water from the leaves of a plant
Trophic level	a feeding level, e.g. herbivore is a primary consumer
Veins	blood vessels, with valves, that return blood to the heart
Wavelength	the length of one complete cycle of a wave – or from crest to crest
Work	work is done if a force causes movement

Useful Websites

You may find some further interesting information at any of the sites listed below.

www.schoolscience.co.uk/content

www.purchon.com

www.s-cool.co.uk

www.webschool.org.uk

www.creative-chemistry.org.uk

www.letts-education.com

www.gcse.revisionsearch.co.uk

www.revision-notes.co.uk

www.revise.it

www.projecteducation.co.uk

www.educate.co.uk

www.nabss.org

www.gcse.com

Index

First published in Great Britain in 2002 by Virgin Books Ltd and Letts Educational Ltd

Virgin Books Ltd
Thames Wharf Studios
Rainville Road
London
W6 9HA

Letts Educational Ltd
Chiswick Centre
414 Chiswick High Road
London
W4 5TF

Copyright © 2002 Virgin Books Ltd/Letts Educational Ltd
Design and Illustration © 2002 Virgin Books Ltd/Letts Educational Ltd

Every effort has been made to trace the copyright holders and obtain permission for the use of copyright material. The authors and publishers will gladly receive information enabling them to rectify any error or omission in subsequent editions.

All rights reserved. No part of this text may be reproduced, stored in a retrieval system, or transmitted in any form or by any means, electronic, online, internet, mechanical, photocopying, recording or otherwise, without the prior permission of the copyright owners.

This book is sold subject to the condition that it shall not, by way of trade or otherwise, be lent, resold, hired out or otherwise circulated without the publisher's prior written consent in any form of binding or cover other than that in which it is published and without a similar condition including this condition being imposed on the subsequent purchaser.

A catalogue record for this book is available from the British Library.

ISBN 0 7535 0668 8

Prepared by *specialist* publishing services, Milton Keynes
Printed and bound in Great Britain by Clays, Suffolk

Letts Educational Ltd is a division of Granada Learning Ltd, part of the Granada Group.